Rachel

dear,

THE GREAT BRITISH SEXPERT'S 101 SEX TIPS

A GUIDE TO PLEASING YOUR MAN

Thankyou for giving me the idea for this

Rebecca Dakin

book – I got there in the end!

Much Love

Rebecca xxx

www.thegreatbritishsexpert.co.uk

First published in paperback 2016

ISBN: 978-1-911505-00-6

Cover Design: Bjarne Tungland

Published by Goldcrest Books Int. Ltd:
publish@goldcrestbooks.com
www.goldcrestbooks.com

DISCLAIMER

I'm not suggesting that pleasing a man should be a one-way thing. However, in every relationship, regardless of gender, there are inevitably some times when you choose giving pleasure as your mission. That said, many of these tips bring mutual pleasure.

One thing you should never do is anything that you don't feel comfortable with. If you try something and it doesn't feel right, then it's not right for YOU. And that's OK. Do not feel obliged to try everything in this book: see it more as a menu of ideas...

Sexual health should be of paramount importance, so hygiene, birth control and protection from sexually transmitted diseases should be first and foremost in any sexual relations. For further information visit the following website www.brook.org.uk

The illustrations in this book are not to be taken as endorsement by any individual, programme or company for my book. I have no affiliation or association with the programme or contestants. I am merely someone who has been inspired and enjoyed baking some of my favourite recipes. The 'saucy facts' are meant for a bit of fun and are not meant to be taken literally neither are they guaranteed to work for everyone. Also please note that I am not a doctor, nor have I done any independent research with individuals myself, however, the information here and much more is widely available on the internet.

Be who you are and say what you feel because those who mind don't matter and those who matter don't mind

Dr. Seuss

It is never too late to be what you might have been

George Eliot

Our Life is a creation of our mind

Buddha

I dedicate this book to my dear friend Thomas, who helped make all this possible and whose ongoing friendship, support and encouragement has been invaluable.

CONTENTS

THANKS

With special thanks to Rachel Elnaugh who, as my business mentor in 2011, placed a piece of paper in my hands with the book title 101 Sex Tips, telling me that was my next book title. *I did it finally!*

Also huge thanks to the talented and beautiful Dr Brooke Magnanti who despite being extremely busy with her projects took the time to write such a detailed flattering Foreword for my book. I am honoured and blessed to know her. I am extremely grateful to Emily Dubberley for her extemporary editing skills; for polishing my book, organising it and for putting me in touch with the talented Leila Nihill who created the quirky, fun, illustrations, and who thought my writing was so descriptive I didn't need drawings of bodies. My thanks to both of you. I express sincere gratitude and thanks to Bjarne who bought my cover idea to life with his unique quirky style.

Last but by no means least a big thank you to Sarah Houldcroft for her patience and hardwork putting this book together and making it print and digital ready. Sarah you have been an absolute star!

FOREWORD

DR BROOKE MAGNANTI
A.K.A BELLE DE JOUR

The first time I met Rebecca, I knew she was my kind of woman.

Hey now, dirty minds… not like that! (Well, maybe a little.) She is fierce, funny, and fabulous. And much more. I knew her work already, from her appearances on *Big Brother's Bit on the Side*, various other T.V shows and social media presence. What I hadn't expected about meeting her in person after years of batting mutual admiration back and forth on the internet, was to sit down with someone who was so up-front honest with it.

We shared stories and swapped insights over lunch and cocktails, and I knew from the get-go that this woman could really have a positive influence on the debates and discussions around sex in this country. Because when it comes to talking about, and writing about, sex there is still a lot of stiff-upper-lip attitude to contend with. As an

American living in the UK, I have to say hand on heart you don't often meet a British woman who combines all these qualities and still has the ability to make everyone in her presence feel like they are the star of the show – but somehow, Rebecca not only does this, but she does it in great style as well.

So when I heard she was writing a new book I had to find out more. And when I finally saw the result? Well, it doesn't disappoint. Because anyone these days can pick up a magazine and be made to feel like we're 'doing it wrong'. Worse, so many writers are rushing to file copy that makes us feel terrible about ourselves, and skip down the path of making readers feel bad, in order to keep them clicking, linking, and buying. It's a genuine breath of fresh air to read someone who thinks the opposite: that we could all be 'doing it right'. That the tools to a great sex life, namely open and honest communication skills combined with some honest, pulling-no-punches tips, are within everyone's grasp.

If you have also had the pleasure of meeting Rebecca, then I don't need to go on – you already know the qualities of which I write. But for those who may only have caught a few minutes of her appearances and wondered what all the 'Great British Sexpert' fuss is about, or even have yet to encounter her work, then you are in for a treat. Because Rebecca is like the awesome sister or best friend we all wish we had, but only a few of us can lay claim to.

Her presence is as warm and welcoming as she is honest. Rebecca has experience, good humour, and empathy to spare, and she is here to tell you about how your sex life can go from so-so to Fire Down Below.

It isn't simply Rebecca's professional experience with men that makes her an expert. It's also her way with people. Anyone can tell you a list of tricks, but not everyone can teach you how to use them in the best ways possible. Making that connection between the mental and the physical is what Rebecca's work is all about. What use are lists of exotic positions, without confidence? How can couples reconnect when they aren't feeling serious passion? Great sex is so much more than a complicated yoga class for the impossibly flexible – it is about really connecting with your partners, and opening your mind as well as opening… well, you know.

Sex is one of those human pleasures, like good food, that not only ticks the basic, biological needs for our continued existence, but can also be raised to high art. Sure, you could be settling for the quick piece of toast or the furtive takeaway, but there can also be so much more. Rebecca shows us how to go from the fast-culture, fast-food experience to something approaching Michelin-starred sex.

And to be frank… who wouldn't want a little of that?

Dr Brooke Magnanti

PREFACE

Regardless of gender or sexuality, we all deserve to love and feel loved, enjoy intimacy and have satisfying sex (even if that means solo sex). Sex is something that unites us and connects us, with ourselves and with others – none of us would be here without sex, and we should be able to express ourselves freely without fear, judgement or feelings of inadequacy.

People are forever trying to box people in to what is right and what is wrong, what is 'normal' and what is not. However, the truth is there is no right and wrong way to do things when it comes to sex, and there is no 'normal' or 'abnormal'. There are billions of people in the world who are all unique and it's about finding people who like the same things as you. There's nothing wrong with 'vanilla' and there's nothing wrong with kink or BDSM (bondage, domination, sadism and masochism). Between consenting adults it really is a case of, 'whatever floats your boat'.

This book is for anyone who wants to give pleasure to a man, whether you are a man *(N.B. depending on gender many, but not all, of these tips will be relevant for everyone),* woman (both cissexual and transgender, because being a woman is who you are inside). It's for those who understand the mutual pleasure that is enjoyed through giving, and knowing how to ask for what you want, in equal measure.

It's for anyone who is fed up with magazines and their so-called 'sex advice' about how we should all orgasm to have good sex, and try having sex standing on our head, to keep things exciting and all the other crazy stuff designed to make us feel inadequate, boring and not adventurous enough…. those who feel they don't fit in, people who don't conform with the idealised media view of sex, people who wonder if they are 'doing it' right, or if there's something wrong with them. It's for people who want to reconnect with a partner, enhance their sex life, explore new sensations as well as maybe revisiting some simple things that can get forgotten over time; and those who are ready to explore sex with men for the first time.

I once felt like I didn't fit in, and through exploring my sexuality I built my self-esteem and empowered myself. It's my mission to use my experience to do that for people today.

WHY THE GREAT BRITISH SEXPERT?

I spent a decade as an escort, travelling the globe, during which time I learned a lot about what men of various nationalities really wanted – and what they complained their sex lives lacked. Even though I spent time with men from diverse cultures and countries, there was one thing that they all sought and that was basic intimacy, affection and that feeling of being desired and appreciated. There are various levels of intimacy and sex is only a small part of it. I also learnt what it was the men I dated were lacking which most likely meant their partners were dissatisfied also! I have published a book about my experiences and 'sexploits' as a sex worker, *The Girlfriend Experience*. And, of course, I've learned a lot through my private sex life too.

My work now encompasses helping people in all areas of dating, mating and relating. One day I can be working one-to-one, 'out in the field' so to speak, in a very practical hands on way with someone who lacks confidence, the next day I can be called up by Sky T.V or other media to give my 'Sexpert' advice on a broader level to the nation, to then working with someone across the globe via Skype who is dealing with infidelity in their relationship or I could be building an online dating profile for someone who is struggling with online dating.

As an author, Master Practitioner in NLP, and qualified hypnotherapist, my work also involves changing people's negative beliefs about sex and intimacy, which can range from beliefs handed down from generations that sex is bad (sometimes these are religious beliefs) to some people feeling that they are not worthy enough for love, or that there is something wrong with them, to those who hold back and put up walls to avoid getting hurt, whilst in the meantime not allowing themselves to fully experience what sex has to offer on an emotional level, to name but a very small selection of beliefs that affect our love and sex life and in turn our general well being.

I offer sex and relationship education and coaching using powerful meditation techniques to help people build confidence for sex, intimacy and orgasm, enhance sex, connect with their own sexuality and reconnect with their partners.

Though I'm proud to be British, unfortunately, there is still a stigma in this country around sex.

It is still deemed acceptable for a man to have multiple sexual partners but not women: often in the views of both men and women. People who are anything other than heterosexual, still face abuse from small-minded people. As an ex-escort, I'm only too aware of sex work stigma.

I want to help fight this stigma, and show that Great Britain can have great sex – and that some of us Brits have tips to share with the rest of the world too.

This book is the product of over 20 years' experience in the sex industry exploring my own sexuality both inside and outside of my time as an escort. While there is no 'one size fits all' approach to sex, the tips should help give you some ideas to explore with your lover – and help you communicate more easily about your mutual needs. When it comes to sex, communicating your desires and boundaries, fantasies and needs is the starting point from which great sex can grow. My book is designed to give you a starting point for discussion – and play.

WHY CAKES, SEX AND TEA?

Cakes, sex and tea; for me there is a strong link between them and as a true Brit these are three of my favourite things.

Cakes, desserts, biscuits and pastries are an indulgence. They are naughty, sweet and can be creamy, fruity or chocolaty, with many delicious ingredients that can be bought into sex play if one so desires.

The feel-good chemical, serotonin, that is present when we consume sugar, is also the same chemical that is released in the brain when we have sex! When we devour our partner we essentially eat them, we nibble them, suck them, lick them and enjoy them.

Sweet treats aside from filling you up, are devilishly delicious, and are perfect to be savoured alongside tea, and we all know what comes after sex….? A nice cup of Rosy Lee!

The illustrations in this book have all been inspired by some of my favourite recipes and dishes from an iconic British baking programme. All the recipes can be found online.

INTRODUCTION

Apparently we Brits are prudes, with our stiff upper lips. Not any more, in fact some of us are decidedly loose, and I'm going to prove it to you! I have spent almost a quarter of a century gaining 'hands on experience' both on a professional and personal level of pleasing men. For the first time ever I am going to document some unique tricks from the sex trade, dispelling some of the myths about what we *think* men want, to show you what they *really* want.

This book is for women and men of all ages who want to explore sex and intimacy and learn how to bring out their sexy side. We'll start getting warm with the basics (or 'signature moves') before moving on to things that take a little more effort (technical challenges) and ending with some showstoppers. After all, sometimes you want to keep things simple and other times you may feel inclined to put the work in to really impress.

Keep a look out for the tips with stars, they are my Top Tips!

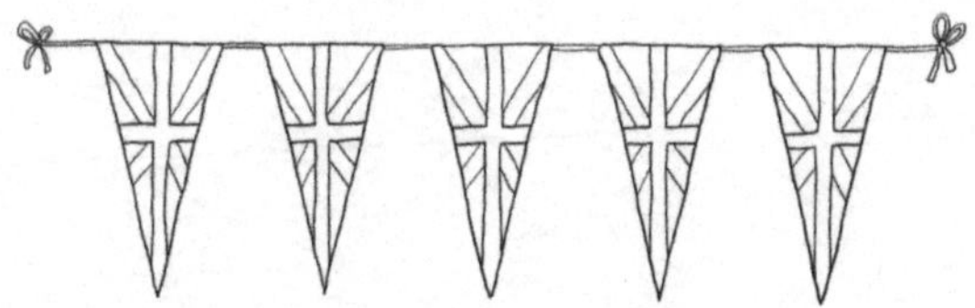

SIGNATURE MOVES

I was pleasantly surprised to find that during my decade as a courtesan the most pleasures I gave men were based on very basic intimacy. To have the best sex you need to be in tune with your partner, be tactile, inquisitive and have a genuine desire to please and be pleased.

There's a reason why 'the girlfriend experience' is one of the most requested services from escorts. My current work as a Sexpert also confirms this. Men want to please, they want sex to be fun, and want lots of intimacy. These tips and techniques will equip you with the basics from which intimacy – and great sex – can grow. See them as 'sweet treats' for your man.

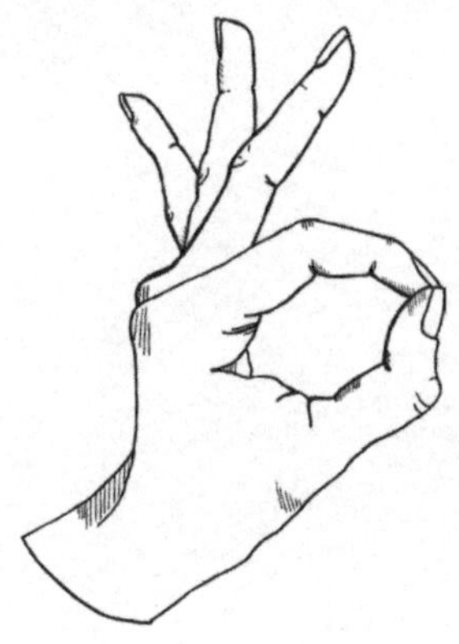

TIP 1

MASTER THE BASICS

Remember *there is no right or wrong way to do things.* It's about experimenting and wanting to give pleasure. So relax, experiment, explore and enjoy. I've always been inquisitive and experimental and it's always reaped rewards. Let go of that fear of doing things wrong and you'll learn what your partner likes.

TIP 2

There are so many erogenous zones and you can have lots of fun finding them. Often people don't know where their own are. Everyone is different; so don't expect every man to like every one. If you say, "This is supposed to be an erogenous zone but it seems a bit weird to me," it's unlikely he will respond. Instead, learn through exploration of his body.

Don't just think you can dive on into licking behind his knee and he'll go wild. Erogenous zones are used to build anticipation. Start by laying him on his back and deep French kissing him before starting your journey of exploration of his body – and pay close attention to his body's response as much as his moans and groans.

This is especially something I recommend to couples I am working with that are new in a relationship and/or lack sexual experience, or couples looking to bring the spark back, because it's a great starting point for building desire and intimacy.

TIP 3

See his body as a big 'dot to dot'. Kiss, lick and caress the areas in between and work from one erogenous zone to the other.

Listen for short intakes of breath, biting of the bottom lip, tilting the head back, holding your head/hand in the spot you're at, groans, tension, movement of his body closer to you and whispered words of appreciation. If you can, watch his face too – he's likely to show his enjoyment...

TIP 4

You can't get more intimate than someone's face. It's where so many of our senses are. We smell, see and hear, speak, kiss all from our head/face, so this is an area not to be missed, but one that's often overlooked.

Kiss his eyelids and gently suck them. Flutter your eyelashes on his cheeks to give delicate butterfly kisses. Feathering light kisses all over his face while you are holding his head/face can be highly erotic and a deeply intimate act. Of course, there are other parts of your body that he will probably welcome on his face, but that's for later.

TIP 5

Men can have very sensitive scalps, especially if they have very short hair or are shaved. Start off by putting both your hands on his head when you are kissing, to pull him deeper into you, and as you carry on kissing you use your fingertips with firm pressure to circulate his scalp; as though you were giving him a massage. If he has hair, grab it with your fingers close to the scalp and *gently* tug at the roots. A head massage can also get him a bit woozy, relaxed and in the mood as part of foreplay.

TIP 6

Our lips have hundreds of nerve endings in them. Trace the outside of his lips with your tongue, and gently suck both the upper and lower lip one after the other, then both together. Lightly kiss the outline of his lips, and lick where they join together. Try and penetrate your tongue through his closed lips – though don't be surprised if they open for you...

TIP 7

Some men have sensitive ears. You can gently use your tongue to trace the outline of the ear, and even penetrate the ear hole.

Breathing directly into his ear and groaning the same sounds of pleasure that you make when you're thinking of enjoying your favourite ice cream, talking dirty (tip 12) and gentle nibbling of lobes and licking behind the ear can also be highly erotic.

TIP 8

Once you have gone to the back of the ears you can trace your tongue down his neck. Kiss him and form suction with your mouth. You want to get to that point where you don't leave a mark (unless it's somewhere discreet and he wants you to) but if you were sucking and nibbling any more, then you would.

There's a reason 'love bites' are enjoyed and it's not about ownership! Tracing the nape of his neck with your tongue or kisses will send shivers down his spine.

Holding his head firmly and pulling him closer to you whilst you explore his neck will show him a little bit of dominance that may well drive him wild.

TIP 9

A SIMPLE SPONGE

A bath with loads of bubbles is great foreplay. Water and bubbles can help your hands glide over each other more easily. Bathing each other is very erotic. It's a great starting point for breast massage (tip 60) and anal play (tip 77). Experiment with different essential oils and bubble baths. *However, make sure you don't get them anywhere intimate to avoid irritation.* A soapy sponge can be a great addition to play: talk about getting your man into a real lather.

Victoria Sandwich

THE PERFECT VICTORIA SANDWICH

VICTORIA SPONGE

200g softened butter
200g caster sugar
4 eggs
200g self raising flour
Strawberry jam

OPTIONAL SAUCY EXTRAS AND FACTS

Add some whipped cream to play with and...
100g fresh strawberries

Aside from strawberries symbolising fertility with their many seeds and cute heart shape, these little beauties are full of iron, fibre, folic acid and potassium making them a perfect fruity choice to boost libido and fertility.

TIP 10

Another way to get you both in the mood is to share a shower, and wash each other. You can use the shower gel to foam up and have a fumble. The spray from the shower can also be used to stimulate the clitoris; the closer it is to your clit the more intense it is. If there's any reason to invest in a power shower, this is it!

Make sure you get your hair wet if you can, because many men love the carefree wet look.

TIP 11

After bathing you can smother yourself with scented lotion so your skin is silky smooth ready for playtime. In fact why not let him rub it in, and massage you with it?

If you have sensitive skin try an organic pure oil; like Jojoba. There is something very sensual about slippery bodies.

TIP 12

RECIPE FOR SEDUCTION

Guys go wild for dirty talk. Tell him explicitly what you want to do to him, with a devilish smile playing on your lips to ramp up the heat and get him in the mood! It doesn't need to be anything crazy it could be as simple as "I want your cock inside me," or "kiss me now, I want to taste you."

A PASSION FRUIT AND LIME CHARLOTTE RUSSE

SAUCY FACT

Vanilla, one of the ingredients in this indulgent dessert, is an aphrodisiac and it is reported that in the 1800's Dr John King advised a hefty swig of vanilla extract before bedtime would ensure sexy time.

Passion Fruit & Lime Charlotte Russe

TIP 13

When I was working away as an escort I used to really miss my boyfriend and pine for him, so this next tip is what I used to do to show him he was on my mind…

Leave notes around the house or in his work clothes: for a little bit of excitement or to build up anticipation. Write down what you want to do to him on slips of paper, and put them in his bag, jacket or trousers so that he finds them when he's at work.

Make sure that you put them in a place you know he will find them *(and no one else will!)*. You might put one in his trouser pocket where you know he keeps his change.

If you're putting them around the house, once again make sure that he will find them. If you're going to be away overnight, put one in his side of the bed for him to find. How about leaving him a small packet of lube with a cheeky note encouraging him to masturbate, 'think about me x'.

TIP 14

Text sex: is a great way to get your partner in the mood. Start teasing him throughout the day saying what you are going to do with him when he gets home from work. This way you build excitement and anticipation.

Talk about something that you are doing or want to do – that reminded you of him. E.g; 'Just been browsing lingerie and was thinking about you. I bought some sexy lace undies – and I'm thinking about what I can do to you later…' If you have been shopping you can then text him a photo of the lingerie.

See how dirty you can get. Express to him what you are going to do to him, and wait for him to text back with what he wants to do to you. This is great foreplay; it's simple and fun.

TIP 15

HAVE CONFIDENCE

Feeling comfortable naked is important if you want to enjoy good sex and really connect with your lover. Ask your partner what he loves about your body and learn to build your confidence. Men don't care what size or shape you are; they care whether you are confident with how you look – it's one of the biggest turn-ons. If you insist on having the lights out or diving under the covers it can be a big turn-off.

Do whatever it takes to find that confidence with your body. Being aware of your assets and good parts of your body and focusing on them will help, but ultimately listen to what your partner says, the bits that he likes, and try and focus on this when you're getting naked, not the bits you don't like. *Whilst your focus is on yourself and your body you won't be in the moment or enjoy sex and intimacy.*

Don't forget that while you are maintaining eye contact he will be looking in your eyes and not so much elsewhere! There are various alternative therapies to help boost confidence, it's something I can help with and many other people are qualified in this field.

If this is a problem for you, this is probably one of the most difficult tips here; however, if you address this issue, it will have the biggest positive impact on your sex life, well being and happiness. It will literally transform your life in the most amazing way possible!

Midsummer Dream Wedding Cake

A MIDSUMMER DREAM WEDDING CAKE

SAUCY FACTS

Oh boy, where to start with this fabulous creation! This recipe is packed with aphrodisiacs....

Ginger to increase sexual prowess, rhubarb, especially when mixed with other aphrodisiacs can work well as it sets the blood into motion. The beta-carotene in carrots is said to feed sexual appetites, and cinnamon and pistachio nuts are both known for increasing sexual desire, increasing both physical and sexual appetite, whilst apricots boost sex drive and fertility in women. Pineapple was historically used to cure impotence and is still used today to help provide energy for optimal sex drive. Sweet potatoes are high in potassium meaning they can help curb any anxiety about sexual performance and help reduce stress. It is reported that beetroot increases blood flow to the genital area.

This cake on your wedding night should have you both ravishing each other all night, if one hasn't indulged in too much champagne!

TIP 16

You can always use dimmed lights, they don't have to be bright, or use candles but you do both need to be able to see *(unless you're specifically using a blind fold – which is a great way to make darkness sexy – more about that later)*. A softer lighting can create ambience and be very sensual.

Try scented candles. Ylang ylang is an essential oil that acts as an aphrodisiac and you can get candles scented with the fragrance.

TIP 17

Avoiding eye contact shows embarrassment, discomfort and a lack of confidence. Instead, look him in the eye in a dreamy, seductive way *(you can temporarily take your mind else where if you need to – pretend you're someone else, or he's someone else, or even think about savouring and indulging in your favourite dessert).*

Eye contact shows that you desire him and are confident (even if you're not, it will give the illusion that you are) Eye-gazing helps you connect on a deep, intimate level.

Always assume he'll be looking at you, and try to make sure that whatever you are doing he can see you. It can be highly erotic for your man if you look up at him from under your lashes with your head tilting down, especially if you're playing with his cock. If you look at your man while you are having sex with him, touching him, sucking his cock; you will connect with him. It's very powerful and makes your experience much more intense.

One of my coaching clients hadn't looked at her partner for years when they had sex, she had always kept her eyes closed, and she wasn't sure why. He had problems with ejaculation; however, the simple thing of opening her eyes allowed them to connect and the sex they now have is intense, much more mutually satisfying and he no longer has problems with ejaculation.

TIP 18

BUILDING THE HEAT

During my time as an escort I found that stroking was a part of intimacy that most men really enjoyed. I don't mean obvious sexual parts instead, stroke up and down the torso, legs and arms.

While this can be lovely for post-sex intimacy, it's also something that you can do to get things warmed up. If you're sitting watching TV with your hand on his leg, start by slowly and lightly stroking up and down and then get closer and closer to his crotch and inner thigh. You'll soon find him twitching down below, and before long, there's a good chance he'll want to ravish you.

MINI PEAR PIES

SAUCY FACTS

The curvy shape of the pears in this recipe should get him thinking about your womanly curves, however, it's the added spice of the cinnamon that will get you both in the mood for a sexy time.

Mini Pear Pies

TIP 19

Many guys love the feel of long hair trailing down them, but they also like to see you, so always be conscious of that and make sure you keep your hair to one side.

Some like the feel of hair trailing down their body so it's another sensation you can add in there while you are using your hands and other body parts on him.

TIP 20

Dry humping is very under-rated. Sometimes the friction of clothing can be very arousing – and there's something about holding back that can bring back sexy memories of those early teenage fumblings. If you're lying on the sofa together, slide a leg over his and start moving and grinding your pelvis on his leg/thigh. This is likely to get him very aroused. For women, getting the seam of your crotch in the right place on or near your clitoris may even lead to orgasm (and indeed, some men can come while it's still 'in their pants' too).

While you are grinding on him, use one hand to trace the outline of his cock through his trouser and to rub it. See if you can make a wet patch come through his jeans (though men have varying amounts of pre-cum so don't feel bad if this doesn't happen). As things heat up, straddle him and grind up and down, tilting your pelvis back so that your parts can rub together through your jeans.

Another thing you can do is both lie flat with your legs together (with one of you on top), and just enjoy the feeling of his erection pressing into you and rock your pelvises together to increase the sensation.

TIP 21

Once the clothes come off, don't just go straight for penetrative sex. Instead, lie on top of him when he is face down and enjoy the sensation of your body contouring his.

Try to get as much of your body as possible in contact with his, even your feet. It's a great position to nibble his ears and/or neck from. You can also do this when covered in oil or body lotion.

Remember that our skin is our biggest organ, so maximum skin contact is extremely erotic. It's almost a full 'body to body' massage.

TIP 22

Say my name: men love hearing you say their name during sex. It really makes things more intimate. Just make sure you get the name right *(so don't use his name if you've recently broken up with someone in case the wrong name slips out!)*

Murmuring your partner's name is very good for his ego, as he knows that you are there in the moment with him and not thinking about the big pile of washing!

TIP 23

ADD A LITTLE SPICE

Have you got some time to yourselves? Tell him how much you want him. Now. 'Quickie' sex when it's spontaneous can be a great way to keep intimacy when you always seem pushed for time.

Quickies should never be a substitute for quality bedroom time but are a great added extra to keep connection in between time.

Cardamom, Pistachio & Coffee Swiss Roll

A CARDAMOM, PISTACHIO AND COFFEE SWISS ROLL

SAUCY FACTS

This dessert is laden with ingredients to heat things up between the sheets.

The cardamom spice has been used for many years as an aphrodisiac, and it increases blood flow whilst also helping with anxiety so a great one for erectile dysfunction and premature ejaculation. The pistachio and coffee together will assist with energy levels and desire.

TIP 24

Try writing out some cheques for him, (*not real ones*). A hand-made notebook in the style of a chequebook, stapled together, can bring spontaneity when you least expect it. The idea being he can cash them in when he's in the mood.

For example one could be for a blowjob, one could be for you dressing up in suspenders, one could be for him feasting on your body and pleasuring you, anything you both like to do. In fact why not write one for yourself so you also have cheques to cash in with him.

This one works well with couples I work with that want to add some spontaneity to their sex life, and those that feel uncomfortable initiating intimacy.

TIP 25

Tickling: there is a fine line between pleasurable tickling and discomfort, so have a play and find the borderline level because it's a sensation that shouldn't be missed.

Many people have an area on their neck that when it's nibbled it tickles, and it's pleasurable but almost unbearable in a good way, and that's what you are aiming for.

For some it's their waist, inner thigh or pubic area. Tantalise and tease the ticklish areas but do it cautiously and watch the physiology of your partner, so you make sure that it's pleasurable for him.

TIP 26

This could end up in a play fight, particularly if he thinks you've over-stepped the mark with your tickling. If so, it's game on! Sex should be fun and playful. This is a fun type of mild foreplay and it increases the intensity and intimacy.

If you're straddling him and trying to pin his arms down to tickle him and if he's getting out of your grasp, try the 'school girl pin' which is when you kneel on his arms between the shoulder and elbow, with your bum on his chest locking his arms above his head and holding his wrists with your hands. You'll find you've pinned him down good and proper, and he'll have to succumb to you as the seductress.

TIP 27

Pretend penetration from behind: if you're feeling in a cheeky, naughty mood (*which is most of the time for me!*), pretending to hump him from behind can get him going.

If he's lying on his front, lie on top of him and thrust your pelvis on his behind, if you're naked it could end up with him on all fours – and who knows where that might lead...

TIP 28

If he's on top and you're in missionary, really grab his buttocks and pull them towards you, and alternate between his hips and buttocks.

He will go crazy knowing that you want him inside you deeper and deeper. You may find it a turn-on to feel his buttock muscles clenching as he's pumping away.

TIP 29

DON'T FORGET DECORATION

Dressing up shows you are willing to make an effort to look your best for your lover. It's important to have quality time as a couple. If you have kids try to get a sitter at least once a month so you can go out for dinner and/or drinks.

When you do go out it's good to make as much effort as you did in the early days. This will make you feel sexy and it will get your man going too. NB: *He should make the effort too; it's a two-way thing!*

FONDANT FANCIES

225g softened butter
225g caster sugar
4 eggs
2 tsp vanilla extract
225g self-raising flour
1-2 tbsp apricot jam
200g marzipan
1 x 500g white fondant icing (ready to roll)
Food colourings of your choice

BUTTERCREAM

250g unsalted butter
300g icing sugar
1 tsp vanilla extract

OPTIONAL SAUCY EXTRAS AND FACTS

The vanilla pod is a mild nerve stimulant and has been known to enhance sensations during sex.

Why not try drizzling dark chocolate over your fancy, ahem, I mean fancies!

Dark chocolate increases our mood and stimulates, however, it does so much more than that. It increases blood flow to sexual organs increasing sensation and desire.

Fondant Fancies

TIP 30

Work out: another tip to get him in the mood is when he gets home from work make sure you have your sexiest gym kit on, and be doing a work-out DVD in the front room. Your man will go wild watching your bits jiggling up and down as you do an aerobics work-out.

You don't want to wear yourself out so you want to get a bit sweaty but not bright red from exhaustion. Make sure your gym kit accentuates his favourite bits.

Finish your work out session with a bedroom session. Exercise boosts your endorphins too, so it's a great stress-buster – which is a great way to lift your libido if you feel it is low or needs a boost.

TIP 31

You don't have to buy lingerie for shopping to be sexy. What about going and trying on some sexy outfits while he watches (or, if you can get away with it, sneaks into the dressing room with you)?

You don't need to have money to buy them. Just give him some imagery that he can save in the 'wank bank' or for when you make love. He might want to take some snaps on his phone too.

TIP 32

When you're out and want to get him going and eager to take you home, tell him you're wearing no underwear.

The more 'inappropriate' the occasion the more it will turn him on… his grandma's birthday dinner should be over in a jiffy when he realises you have no underwear on!

TIP 33

TASTE THE DIFFERENCE

Mouths and lips are erotic as they are used for kissing, nibbling, licking and oral sex. This is why feeding each other can be a very intimate and erotic act.

Try blind-folding each other and doing taste tests with foods that are aphrodisiacs, for example; oysters, asparagus and chocolate. You'll find plenty in this book and more on the internet.

This is fun foreplay and a great way to bond before sex. You may find things will get messy and you can have all sorts of fun licking foods off each other.

ORANGE BUTTERFLY CAKES

SAUCY FACTS

If you want to get an aphrodisiac in, try making them more traditionally using vanilla extract instead of orange.

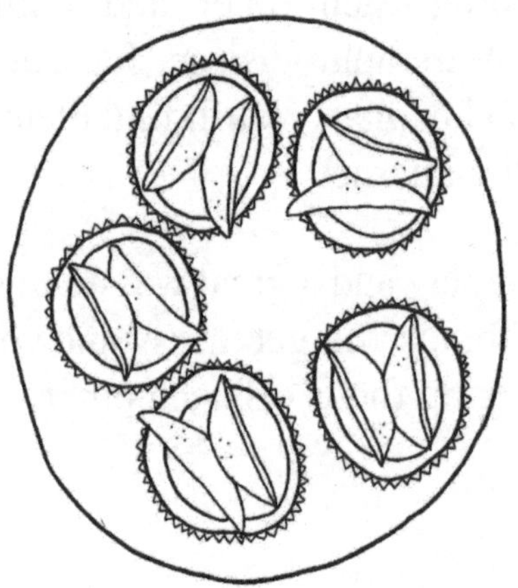

Orange Butterfly Cakes

TIP 34

Anything that you can suck and/or lick that makes guys think of you giving them oral sex is likely to get them going, so if you're going for fingers and toes, simulating oral sex can be very visually exciting.

Lick, suck and trace your tongue up, down and around the length of his finger or big toe. The palms and the arch of the foot are very sensitive areas for nibbling or firm scratches with your nails.

Do be careful of feet though, not everyone likes people going near their feet, and for some it's an area that is too ticklish to be touched.

TIP 35

And then there's more intimate tasting; spitting out semen can be a turn-off with some guys feeling rejected, interpreting it that they taste so vile that you want their juices out of their mouth as quickly as possible. Even if this is true, if it was the other way around, think how you would feel *(though encouraging him to drink pineapple juice can make the experience sweeter for both of you).* So how about making him a fruit smoothie a few hours before hand? 'Semen sourers' include alcohol, cigarettes and spicy foods, so if he's been out on the razzle and had a curry then it's probably not the best time to treat him!

Once semen is in your mouth the quickest way to get rid of it is to swallow it and make sure you have some juice or water by the side of the bed. If you don't want to swallow then this is perfectly fine too. However, it's easier to *not* let him ejaculate in your mouth. If you do want to try and swallow here are some tips.

Make sure the head of his penis is as far to the back of your throat that is comfortable for you. When he ejaculates, swallow it as soon as you feel it coming, and keep swallowing until he has finished.

If you do this straight away you won't taste his semen. The only time you taste it is if you have it in your mouth and you don't swallow straight away or if you spit you will also taste it, as you have to then let it pass across your tongue and taste buds to spit it out!

You can either ask him to let you know when he's about to come and aim at an area on your body, or if you can tell when he's about to come move your mouth away at the last second and compensate by using the hand suction technique (tip 58) to finish him off. Whatever you do don't lose momentum when he is about to ejaculate, either swiftly move to using your hand only and take aim, use both your hand and mouth or continue with just your mouth.

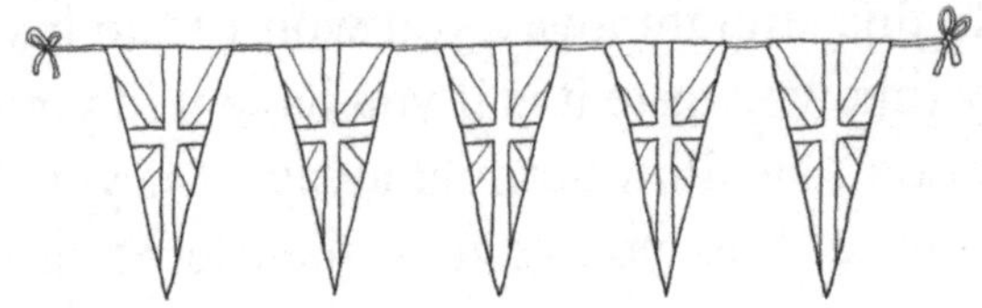

TECHNICAL CHALLENGES

Some sex acts take a little more practice to get right – though half the fun comes from practising. Don't feel bad if you 'get it wrong': remember, there's no such thing as 'wrong' in consensual sex – we're all learning. However, these moves should help show your lover that you really care about their pleasure – and give them an appetite for more.

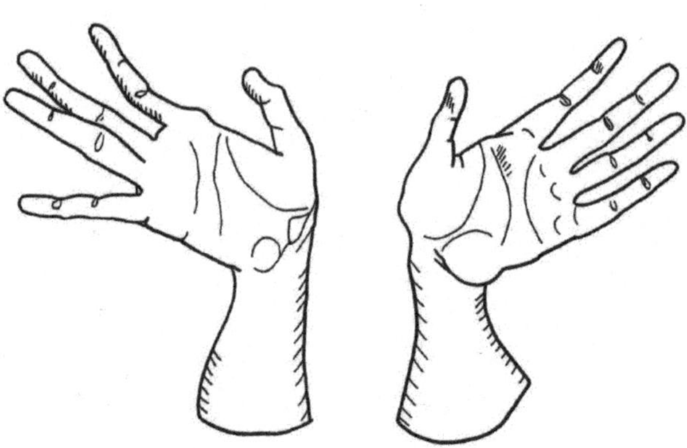

TIP 36

MAGIC MOMENTS

Ladies: even if you can't actually walk in heels, get some for the bedroom. They're great for making your legs look their best. If your man has a foot fetish take him out with you shopping whilst you both choose a pair.

If you don't like the skin on your legs then hold ups or stockings and suspenders (don't forget to put your panties over the top) will give your legs a flawless finish and will excite him even more.

If boots do it for him, it's worth investing in some thigh -high boots for bedroom fun. There's also the boudoir style slip-ons with marabou trim for a more delicate feminine look, however you can't go wrong with a pair of killer stilettos.

CAPPUCCINO CRÈME BRULEES

SAUCY FACT

Did you know that tests have been done to prove that caffeine enhances sexual arousal in women? So if your libido is low, this creamy dessert should get you in the mood to play!

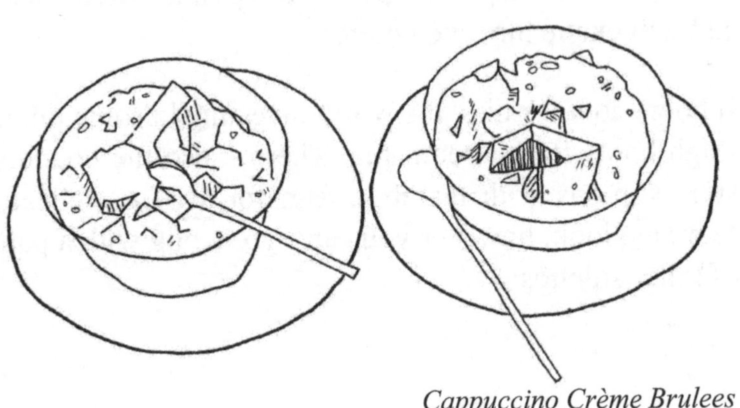

Cappuccino Crème Brulees

TIP 37

Wet 'n' wild! Getting dripping wet can make your clothes hug your body in a way that can drive a man wild. When you are about to get it on, and you're going to freshen up, put either a white vest on or a white t-shirt and go in the shower. Wet yourself including your hair, making sure that your nipples are erect. Dry your body when you get out so that you get rid of the big drips, and leave him with a walking vision of sexy wetness.

You can also add in oil if you want some added shininess. The oil will stop you drying out. If you're going to do this, either spray or cover yourself with oil before you put the t-shirt on and get in the shower. When you come out, you will be wet and slippery, and oiled up ready for action.

Try making love looking in the mirror either in the bedroom or bathroom if you want to avoid messing up the sheets.

TIP 38

When he's thrusting, lift his hips up if he's on top and watch his cock go in and out. Alternate this between looking him in the eye and biting your bottom lip.

If you're on top and guiding him in and out, look down and appreciate the sight of him penetrating you. This is a good time to tell him how good he feels inside you.

TIP 39

Men tend to be visually aroused so make use of any mirrors in the house and, if possible, make sure there's a good one in the bedroom to catch all the action. It will be like watching your own porn movie with you and your partner as the stars!

Watch him watching you in the mirror and angle your body so you can see him pumping. This can be a massive turn-on for both of you. Doggie style is a great position for using mirrors as you both can get a great view.

TIP 40

It goes without saying that lips are very sensual. If you don't like blowjobs then an alternative is to masturbate him close to your lips, so he can imagine. Part your lips and pout them, look him in the eye, and use your hand techniques with lots of lube and make sure that his penis every now and then touches your open lips as if you are about to suck him. Yes it will tease him but trust me there are lots of hand techniques that you can use that will drive him just as wild as oral sex, so if you combine the hand job techniques (tip 58) with lots of lube and licking his cock (shaft and tip) and paying attention around it, you will be able to give him an incredible, memorable sexual experience without even giving him an actual blow job.

If you *are* giving him oral sex, alternate between sucking him and masturbating him making sure that you brush his cock on your lips and that you look at him seductively. Whatever part of his body you are sucking or have your lips on, make sure if possible that he can see you.

TIP 41

Let him come home from work to find you masturbating. That will have him ripping his clothes off quicker than you can say 'Fancy a bit of how's your father?'

TIP 42

GET EXPERIMENTAL

The back is an under-rated erogenous zone – and allows you to explore his neck and ears too. Kissing and nibbling down his back can be very erotic. Try using your breasts and/or nipples and bits to press into his back at the same time, whilst you work your way to his buttocks.

Experiment with different sensations on his back. Lightly use your nails or fingertips to scrape up and down, or try trailing your hair down him. Other sensations to explore are a silk scarf or an ostrich feather.

A 3 TIER NAKED CAKE

SAUCY FACTS

Aside from vanilla, this cake's ingredients also boast a few aphrodisiac berries. Forget the blue pills, blue berries are said to help with erectile dysfunction increasing blood flow to the penis, add in libido boosting strawberries and you're sure to be in for a night of passion, if you've got any energy left after making this cake!

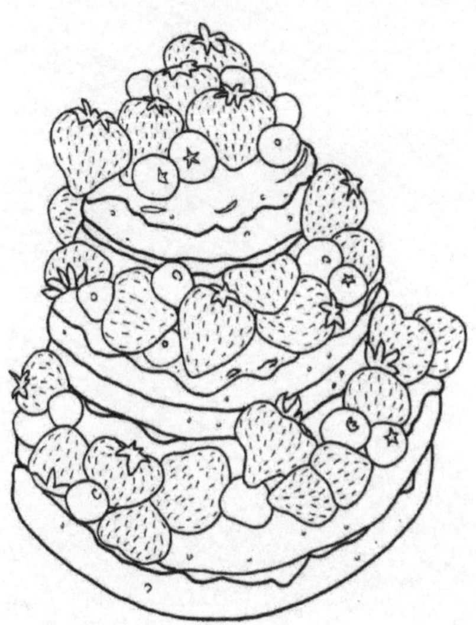

Tiered Naked Cake

TIP 43

After exploring his back, gently part his legs and lift his pelvis so he goes onto all fours. It's a great position to explore his nether regions.

You have full access to his inner thighs, pubic bone, balls, penis and anus, as you can put your head underneath him and alternate between being behind him and underneath him. Try soft flicks with your tongue, licks, kisses, nibbles, touch and massage.

TIP 44

Hold his buttocks firmly, squeezing them together and massaging firmly whilst licking in between his cheeks. You might want to grab them and give them a light nibble. It's a good time to explore anal play if he's up for it (tip 77).

You can lick from the anus up to the top of his buttocks *(health professionals advise using a dental dam – a square of latex – as unprotected 'rimming' is risky)*. It's a great place to reach the inner thigh and the back of the knee too. Part his legs so you have access to his balls from behind.

TIP 45

How much does he trust you? Will he let you near his nether regions with a razor? If so, it can be very satisfying to foam up his balls and shave them so they're smooth. If he won't let you do it, watch him. He might let you trim with scissors the rest of the pubic hair.

If you're struggling to convince him here are 3 reasons he should want to shave/trim.

- It makes him look bigger
- Tell him you'll be more inclined to spend more time down there
- He will be able to feel you more, as pubic hair acts as a barrier and he loses some of the sensation.

Tending to his man-garden is a bonding experience. You may want to let him do the same for you.

TIP 46

The pheromones from sweat are designed to drive *you* wild (as long as it's fresh, of course). His armpit can be an unusual erogenous zone to explore. It may not appeal to you, and if so, that's OK. You can either wait and explore this area when he's fresh out of the shower pre sweat, or bypass that area, and maybe nibble and kiss the armpit crease when his arm is down.

For those that want to get stuck in, lick under your man's arm where the arm creases to fold down (the area before the hair starts). If you really want to embrace this area try burying your face in his armpit and inhale his pheromones while nibbling and licking.

Smell is our most base sense and you may be surprised by how aroused this can make you!

TIP 47

LICK AND LOVE IT

The tip of the penis is the most sensitive area so there is lots you can do here. Pull the foreskin back if he has one, and swirl your tongue around the bulbous head. Give him the visual of your lips around the tip and on it.

The ridge (corona) by the shaft is particularly sensitive, so gently tease your tongue around the edge and under the ridge. The V shape (frenulum) where the skin attaches (or did attach) the foreskin to the penis is also very sensitive. Flick your tongue from the bottom to top of it, not forgetting to look your man in the eye whilst you are doing this. The suction hand job technique (tip 58) can be brought into play here, as that focuses mainly on the tip too. (As an alternative to your mouth, try using a wet finger to lightly brush the 'V' softly.)

MOCHA & TUTTI FRUTTI CREAM HORNS

SAUCY FACT

The plain chocolate and coffee in these creamy horns will be sure to give him the horn. Gerrit?

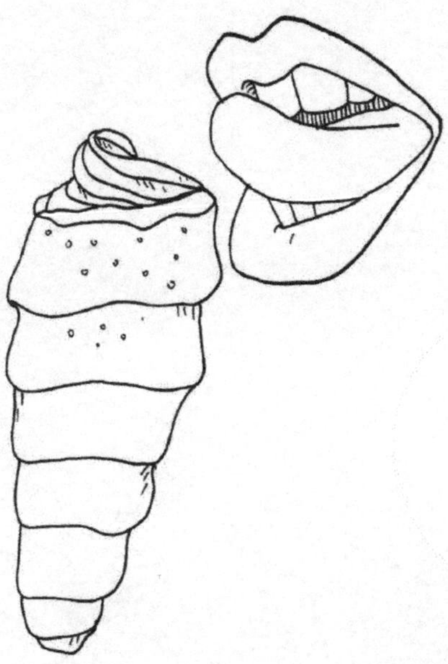

Mocha & Tutti Frutti Cream Cones

TIP 48

Lick the balls gently, and nuzzle into them. Trace your tongue around the area where they attach to his body. The crease where they join is highly sensitive. Very gently suck one ball into your mouth, and very gently give it a light pull, before moving to the next one. If you can, get them both in your mouth and gently suck. This is known as 'tea bagging'.

TIP 49

The perineum is the flat area that joins the balls to the anus – and is very sensitive and full of nerve endings. With him on his back, lick under his balls so that they are resting on your face, and really bury your head in there, reaching with your tongue as far under him towards his anus as you can.

Use your hands to prise his legs apart and raise him up to get access further down. If he raises his hips up towards you, he wants to give you access to his anus and he'll be up for some anal play (tip 77).

Keep your tongue firm so you can apply pressure and, if you're using your fingers, wet them first from your mouth so your fingers can glide and massage that area with no friction. Massage it in a circular motion or from back to front.

TIP 50

HAVE A NIBBLE

Think it's just women who enjoy nipple play? Wrong. Many men have extremely sensitive nipples. They tend to be tougher than women's nipples but start soft and build up to a pressure that's comfortable for him. If there are no signs of any enjoyment after you suck his nipples or tweak them, move along to the next area. However, if he likes it, he won't want you to stop and will make his arousal clear.

You can try using your teeth, gently at first and then getting firmer; or try pinching and rolling his nipples with your fingers. Licking but really pressing your tongue down is a sensation that some men like. Most men who like their nipples played with need it to be quite intense and firm.

HAZELNUT AND ORANGE BISCOTTI

SAUCY FACTS

This nutty biscuit may make you both feel nutty, I mean naughty. Nuts, in general, are a good source of iron and potassium, so can help boost your sex drive.

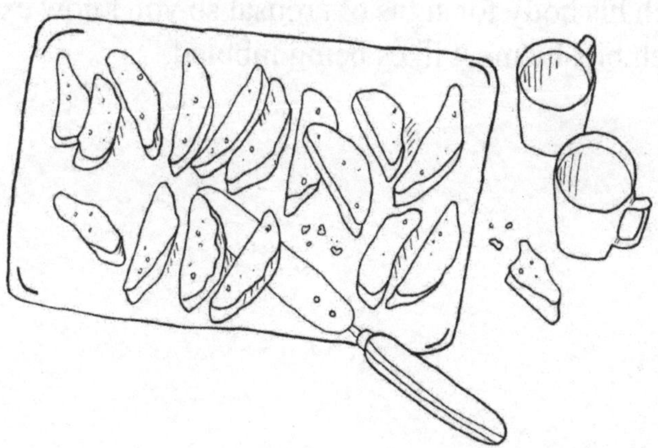

Hazelnut & Orange Biscotti

TIP 51

Try kissing and licking from his pubic bone up to his belly button, then up his torso to his chest and even higher up his neck past his Adam's apple so that he tilts his head back when you get to his chin. If he's reacted and enjoyed the ear nibbling (tip 7) or nipple play (tip 50), you can re-explore either of these areas while you are up there, before making your way back down.

Try to remember to keep eye contact if possible and watch his body for signs of arousal so you know exactly which bits he most likes being nibbled.

TIP 52

The inner joints can be highly sensual so try nibbling behind his knee, his inner thighs, the area that joins the pubic bone to the thigh and the inner elbow. These are very sensitive areas, because they have thinner skin and little, if any, hair.

Start by tracing your tongue lightly on the area and placing gentle feather-light kisses before moving on to firmer pressure. The pubic bone joint is a great place to tease before oral sex. It's so close that he'll tense up wondering when you are going to touch his cock – but you won't – not yet anyway.

This is about building anticipation, getting his body tingling all over and driving him wild.

TIP 53

If he's 'not hard' *(and only then, unless he asks you to do otherwise)* why not try having a gentle chew on his cock. It will soon get hard! Munch it sideways up and down like you would a corn on the cob. Start nice and gentle and increase pressure as you go, being aware not to cause any pain or discomfort.

If and when he gets hard, he won't want your teeth round it, but when it's soft it's quite a nice chewy sensation, and it can get him going.

TIP 54

TWICE AS NICE...

Mutual masturbation can be great foreplay or can be an alternative to penetrative sex. Either lie next to each other or at opposite sides of the sofa/bed. It will drive your man wild watching you pleasure yourself.

Touch yourself where and how you like to be touched and alternate watching him play with his cock, licking your lips and looking him in the eye.

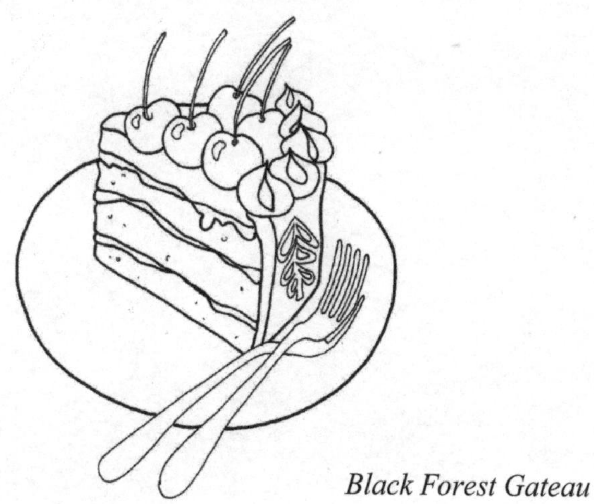

Black Forest Gateau

SAUCY FACT

Cherries are an aphrodisiac and it has been said that some cherries stimulate pheromone production. The antioxidants help your energy levels, and the potassium they provide assists sexual hormone production.

Chocolate and cherries together both create a heady mix of indulgence and naughtiness.

BLACK FOREST GATEAU

265g plain flour
400g caster sugar
65g cocoa powder (unsweetened)
1.5 tsp baking powder
1 tsp bicarbonate of soda
1.5 tsp salt
3 eggs
250ml milk
120ml vegetable oil
3 x 425g tins of black cherries
200g caster sugar
4 tbsp cornflour
1tsp vanilla extract
750ml whipping cream
5 tbsp icing sugar

TIP 55

Don't think mutual masturbation always has to be taken to conclusion. It can be great as foreplay for penetrative sex too. Try licking your own juices off your finger seductively and putting more than one finger inside yourself or using your spit to lubricate yourself and giving a low groan of pleasure.

He'll probably be going wild at this point, and you might want to bring in some 'dirty talk' (tip 12). You can also straddle whilst he still masturbates, as you carry on playing and touching yourself.

If you have breasts, try lowering them onto his cock whilst he is playing with it so that he can feel them lightly brushing onto him. You can also play with his balls and/or get going with anal play (tip 77) for him.

TIP 56

KEEP IT MOIST

Lubricant is great to have fun with. Yes, it's always good to have your own juices, but don't be shy about using lube.

Use it for putting on your bits (including the bottom of your pubic bone) to glide and rub his cock on. Women can use it inside if you want wetness for fingers or his cock – which can make it more comfortable for you too.

Smother it on him during hand jobs, and remember it's an essential for anal play and 'tit wanks' (unless you're giving the latter in the bath). It's good to find one that's water-based and tasteless so you don't mask the taste of your natural juices.

If you're not keen on giving him oral sex why not try flavoured lubrication to make the experience more pleasurable? You can find a selection of lubrications including silicone, water-based and flavoured in my Sexpert Boutique on my website at www.thegreatbritishsexpert.co.uk

CHOCOLATE ORANGE POND PUDDING

SAUCY FACT

Researchers have found that women that eat chocolate every day are reported to have higher libidos than those that don't. If ever there's a reason to indulge in some chocolate then surely this is it! .

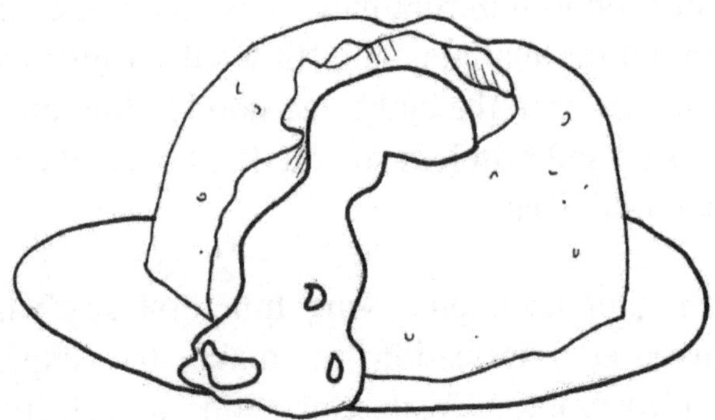

Chocolate Orange Pond Pudding

TIP 57

To mix things up and stop yourself from getting jaw-ache, use a wet hand as an extension of your mouth when giving oral. Where your mouth ends cup your hand, and move it up and down as you do the same with your mouth.

TIP 58

As an escort this was my personal 'showstopper' favourite and it worked a treat every time.

Hand suction makes a great alternative if you don't like giving oral or you get jaw-ache. Make sure that his cock is wet with saliva and/or lubricant and grab his cock like you are about to give him a hand job but, as you bring your hand to the top, close your fist whilst bringing your fingers higher and taking your closed fingers and thumb over the top of the cock.

What you are trying to achieve is a sucking-like sensation so you need to create suction by keeping your fingers and thumb in as much of a fist as you can *(so no air can get through and your fingers and thumb are at full contact)*, while rolling your closed hand up and over the tip of his cock, if you do this slowly he will be begging for more. If you're doing it right you will hear and feel the suction.

This is likely to drive him wild and bring him to a very intense orgasm.

TIP 59

If you want to avoid blowjobs for whatever reason, fear not, you can give the illusion without actually doing it. Firstly, use the suction hand job technique from Tip 58 *(remember a wet suction is what he gets from a blow job, you recreate that feeling with your hand)* but cover the visuals with your hair (or blind-fold him). He won't have a clue what you're doing but he will know it feels amazing.

TIP 60

GET CREATIVE

Why use hands for massage if you're doing it to your lover? If he's a boob man he will love the feel of your breasts rubbing over his skin.

Use your breasts to rub up and down his back, and press one between his bum cheeks. Revisit his erogenous zones with your soft breast tissue. Take them all the way down his legs, past the back of the knees, gently tracing his outline with the weight of your breasts. Or if you're small breasted, use your nipples. You can make this look unintentional if you're using your hands to stroke down his body, or kissing down his body at the same time. If he's on his back you can rub your breasts on his face and down his torso and it's a great starting point for mammary intercourse (aka 'tit wank'). Use some of your own saliva or lubrication and squeeze your breasts around his cock, whilst gently moving up and down. This can also be done with you on your back and him straddling you to put his cock between your breasts and then holding them together, or sideways when you are both lying on your side facing each other. The latter is a great position to try if you struggle with the other options and/or you feel your breasts aren't big enough.

JAPANESE PAGODA TEA TOWER

SAUCY FACTS

This recipe uses rosewater and back in the day Cleopatra used rosewater as an aphrodisiac and it's often used in love potions and fragrances. Roses are a widely recognised as the flower of love and their petals can be eaten. Rosewater can be added to vanilla ice cream for a double hit of aphrodisiac.

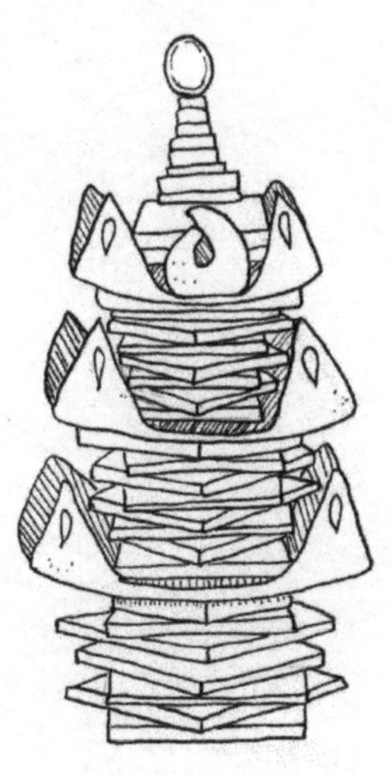

Japanese Pagoda Tea Tower

TIP 61

Those with small breasts will know that men love nipples, many of them more so than breasts, so the alternative here is to make sure that you slide his cock over your nipples so he can feel how erect they are. You can cover your breasts in lube or oil and use his cock to slide over your nipples and breasts.

Make sure that the tip of his cock is unsheathed if it's comfortable for him so that he can feel the maximum sensation.

TIP 62

I think the reason men push women's heads when they receive oral sex is because they like it being done to them when they are giving a woman oral sex. So try it. Taking his head with both of your hands, gently tug him towards you whilst he is going down on you. He will get off on the fact that you are so into what he is doing, and it will further encourage him to carry on, if he thinks you're getting lost in the moment. The more he sounds like he is into it then the firmer you can pull him into you.

If he has a shaved head an experience not to be missed is rubbing his scalp (at a pressure that is comfortable for you) down below in place of his tongue.

When you're wet, the feeling of the light stubble of his head can be surprisingly arousing.

TIP 63

Their penises and their size generally obsess men. So you can pretty much do anything with them as long as you're doing something *(and it's not painful)*. In between a hand/blow job you can slap or tap it lightly on your face or body. It's a sensation that can feel amazing on your body too. Use it to massage yourself with….

TIP 64

Cock rings can help increase blood flow, stiffen up his erection, and create a more intense feeling for him. They work by preventing blood from flowing back down the penis, which in turn helps to make erections feel harder and last longer than normal, which will make your enjoyment last.

You can use your thumb and forefinger to create a cock ring by tightening your finger and thumb and creating resistance at the base of his penis; or you can buy one in my boutique. This isn't something you would do on its own. Instead, do it as part of masturbation, oral sex or penetrative sex.

For penetrative sex, put one hand around his penis at the base as he pumps in and out of you. However, if he has a smaller member, you may find a cock ring more effective as it ensures he can get every inch inside you.

TIP 65

TIMING IS EVERYTHING

Waking up blowjob: if you want him to be fantasising about you all day, before his morning alarm goes off and whilst he is still asleep or dozing, just dive under the covers and give him oral sex, either to completion or if you don't fancy his semen for breakfast wait until you have really got him going and then get on top of him to finish him off. Alternatively give him a hand job.

HOT CHOCOLATE SOUFFLE

SAUCY FACTS

The substance that makes chocolate sensually pleasing is an ingredient called PEA; phenylethylamine. It releases dopamine in the brain's pleasure centres and coincidentally, it peaks during orgasm. Chocolate works chemically to create feelings of euphoria, contentment and excitement. Used in a sweet dessert like this before bedtime will give you both double the pleasure.

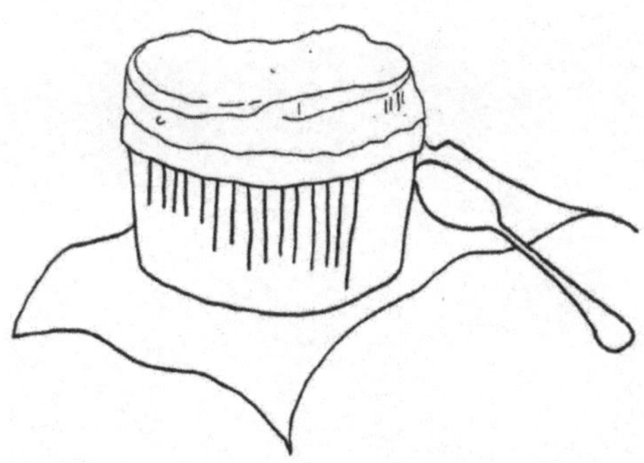

Hot Chocolate Souffle

TIP 66

Try a morning quickie – a fun way to start the day. The great thing about morning sex is that it can be lazy and quick; however, it will put a smile on both of your faces for the day.

If you're spooning he can slip it in from behind, or if you are behind you can put your hands between his legs and touch his balls, and then reach through to his cock. After a little bit of masturbating he should be ready to go, and you can get into the position of your choice.

TIP 67

When couples don't have sex, a lot of tension can build up. As a Sexpert I hear this all the time. Sometimes all that's needed is a 'good shag', and suddenly all is well with the world again. When there's anger and adrenaline after an argument, it's put to much better use when you have sex. It can be raw and exciting, and will help both of you move on. It just takes one of you to initiate it.

The more sex you have the more you want, so you'll never 'feel like it' if you keep avoiding intimacy and feeling stressed.

Instead of arguing when you feel the tension mount up after petty niggles, just kiss him to stop him talking/shouting and ravish him with pure lust as if you haven't had sex for years. Unless the row is a major one (think deal-breaker) I guarantee you this will make you both feel better!

TIP 68

When he steps in the door after a hard day at work, don't speak to him: just deep French kiss him and if he tries to talk, put your fingers lightly on his lips and lead him silently to the bedroom, or rip his clothes off there and then and/or give him oral sex. What a way to wind down from work! Hopefully he'll repay the favour some time.

TIP 69

SWEET TREATS

What other tip can I possibly put here? It has to be 69! Guys love this. Whilst it might not be the best position to receive pleasure from him, as part of foreplay and to get him going, it's worth getting involved.

If you both lie sideways facing, opposite ways, let him pleasure you, whilst you pleasure him with your tongue, and hands, you can fully explore his nether region whilst he does the same for you.

BLUEBERRY, COCONUT AND STRAWBERRY MACAROONS

SAUCY FACTS

Nuts, strawberries and blueberries mean these sweet treats are packed with the good stuff, however, on top of that coconut is thought by the Indians to increase the amount of sperm. Eastern doctors recommend coconut for those suffering from chronic fatigue, so these tasty macaroons should help keep his energy levels up for the bedroom.

Blueberry, Coconut & Strawberry Macaroons

TIP 70

Few things will please him more than the sight of you licking his cock like a lollipop. Without using your hands, start at the base on one side and lick the full length of his penis upwards slowly whilst maintaining eye contact. Then go back to the base and move around a little and do the same. Work your way all around, including getting your tongue in behind his cock. Alternate this with sucking the tip and masturbating him.

TIP 71

As a fun twist, try painting his cock with chocolate sauce and then giving him the 'lollipop' (tip 70). You can get chocolate sauce pens so you can write messages on each other. It's important to remember to play.

SHOWSTOPPERS

There are some tips and techniques that are particularly likely to blow your lover's mind (and I don't just mean great blow jobs). If you want to create memories that will stick in your man's mind forever, it's time to pull out a showstopper – sure to give him a real sugar rush!

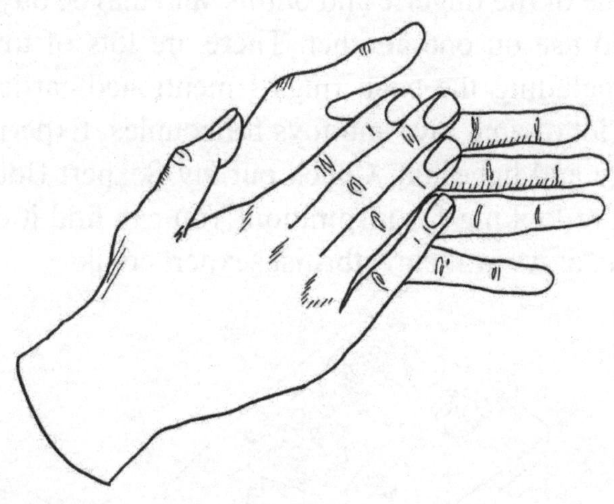

TIP 72

ADD NEW INGREDIENTS

Sex shops have increasingly hit the mainstream over the last decade and are much easier to find – and more pleasant to visit – than they once were. Why not take a trip into town together and have a nosey around? Most staff are very helpful and know all about all of the toys – and there's no need to worry about them judging you as they've seen it all before. You can have fun trying on some of the lingerie and outfits, and maybe buy a toy each to use on one another. There are lots of toys for men including the cock rings I mentioned earlier, but also a lot of anal toys and toys for couples. Experiment, explore and have fun. Check out my Sexpert Boutique if you're looking for inspiration. You can find it on my website at www.thegreatbritishsexpert.co.uk

Figgy Roly Poly with Caramelised Walnut & Honey Ice Cream

FIGGY ROLY POLY WITH CARAMELISED WALNUT & HONEY ICE CREAM

SAUCY FACTS

This is one of my favourite recipes to make! Walnuts are said to give him a stronger erection. Honey, aside from symbolising pro-creation, is a word used to reference one's darling, and for a female, 'honey pot' can be used to reference her vagina. Honey is said to regulate hormone levels and is reported to contain nitric oxide, released in the blood during arousal which means it increases desire. Figs are said to visually look like the female sex organs when cut in half and have long been associated with love and fertility whilst also being an arousing stimulant. Almonds supposedly arouse passion in females.

TIP 73

Showing him how to use your toys on you is a turn-on for him if he wants to learn. If he's unsure about you using toys, it's good to remind him that toys are not substitutes for the real thing, they have their place for fun and exploration in the bedroom.

However, they can never replace a real person with real feelings and real skin. Try getting him involved in the next tip, so you can show their versatility.

TIP 74

Vibrators make great body massagers. Try using them on his perineum and all those sensitive places. The crease between his thighs where his legs meets his torso is a good place to send vibrations to, as are his balls. If he enjoys anal play (tip 77) then he may enjoy penetration with a lubed-up vibrator.

Just remember to thoroughly clean and disinfect toys in between use if you are sharing them.

TIP 75

Taking away sight; one of our key senses, is one of the most erotic things you can do, as all the other senses are heightened and you are left with a heady feeling of anticipation when you can't see what's going on.

Only use a blindfold when there is complete trust.

TIP 76

Sploshing: maybe you've experimented a bit without realising it, by bringing in ice cream, yoghurt or cream into your playtime. Full on 'sploshing' is for those who have a fetish of feeling or watching wet and messy substances being covered on either a naked body or the feeling of the substance through clothes. Why not try cakes and desserts? It's one way to indulge without consuming calories!

It's certainly not for everyone, but if it sounds intriguing to you, then give it a go! Latex sheets or a paddling pool will help you protect your bedding.

TIP 77

A TOUCH OF CHOCOLATE

Assuming your man is up for anal play, make sure that the area is well lubricated. You can use saliva but lubrication is much more effective as the skin inside the anus is thin and can tear easily – not sexy!

The other main trick is to go slowly, and build up to it. For example, start by using your tongue before sticking your tongue in his anus as far as you can *(health professionals recommend using a dental dam)*. If you're not comfortable with this, just use your middle finger to stroke his perineum and then tease the outside of his anus. *Never penetrate unless you can feel he's loose.*

If he's clenching, don't worry: it doesn't mean he's doesn't want to do it, it's just he's not ready at that moment and might mean he has never had it done it before. Keep lightly going around the hole, or leave it there with a little bit of pressure and massage the perineum. You may find he'll loosen up after a while when he realizes you're not going to catch him unawares. It's also something that he may warm to over time when he gets used to the feeling of you being in that area.

CHOCOLATE STARS

SAUCY FACTS

The magnesium in chocolate eases pre-menstrual symptoms, whilst the flavonoids are reported to improve circulation and boost erection. So chocolate is a win win!

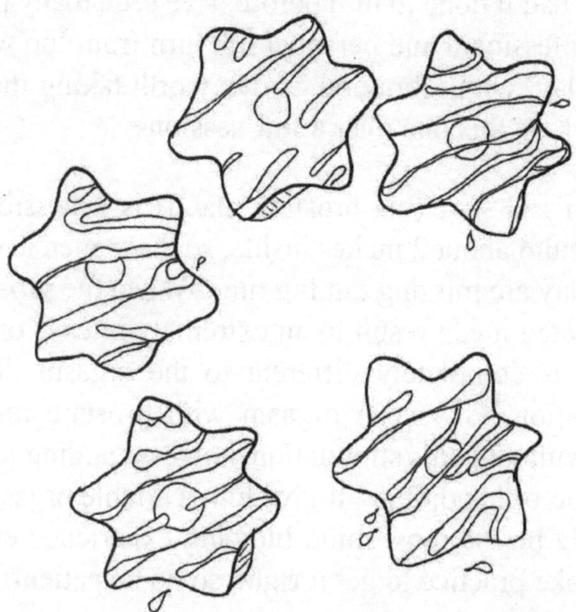

Chocolate Stars

TIP 78

When his anus is loose and the area is fully lubricated, this is where the fun starts. You only put the tip of your finger in, and then you take it out slowly and circle around the outside of his hole. Don't keep putting it in and out or he will feel like he's having a number 2! This is a slow process to build comfort, especially if he hasn't had it done to him before. I've seen many men in my professional and personal life turn from 'no way, to anal play' with vibrators! So it's worth taking the time to work on this one over a few sessions.

A man's G-spot (his prostate gland) is accessible via the rectum about 2 inches inside, so those men avoiding anal play are missing out big time! When the prostate is stimulated it can result in an extremely intense orgasm, and it is completely different to the orgasm through ejaculation. Guys can orgasm with prostate massage even without penis stimulation, however adding it into a blowjob or handjob, will give him a double orgasm and literally be the most mind blowing experience ever! It does take practice to get it right, so do be patient.

Eventually you want to get your finger fully in, and if he's still on his back pull your finger towards you, so its curled, like you are almost beckoning someone to come to you. Circulate and massage the area inside where the finger is touching (not the back wall where the nail will be facing). You should be able to feel the walnut shaped gland.

Those guys experienced with anal play may want more fingers and/or vibrators. More about that later. Be mindful that there will be some men that are very anti anal play, and if you find one, don't feel bad about suggesting it, forget about it and move on.

TIP 79

A SEXY SANDWICH

Women – if your lover has his finger inside you, try looking him in the eye, licking one of your own fingers and popping it in there too. Move your fingers together, and even wrap one of your fingers around him so that you are holding him in there. If he pops his finger out, just guide it back in. Depending on how wet you are and how comfortable you are you can gradually put more fingers in.

This is something you can do for the mutual masturbation. If he is masturbating and you are straddled over him, really open your pussy to him so he can see your lips and see you penetrating your own pussy, then put as many fingers as you want in, one by one, working yourself up, and taking your fingers out to lick them if needs be to add more lubrication (and visual appeal).

RASPBERRY MILLEFEUILLE

OPTIONAL SAUCY EXTRA

All berries are high in antioxidants and a diet high in antioxidants can improve your sexual function, so try adding in some blueberries and strawberries to this dish. If you're feeling extra naughty, drizzle over some melted dark chocolate.

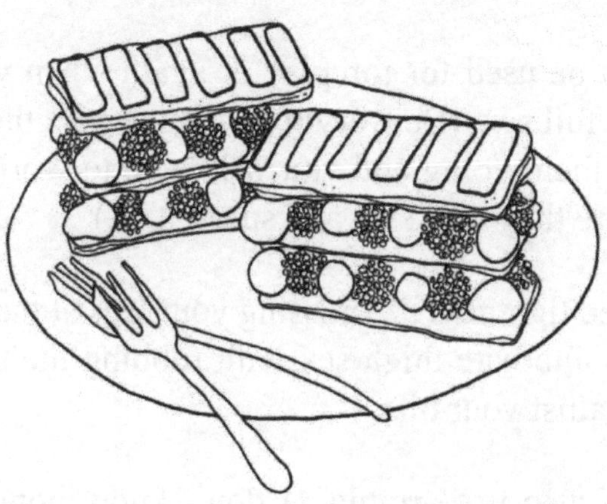

Raspberry Millefeuille

TIP 80

Men just need somewhere tight to put their cock so why not try thigh sex? Keep your legs together, squirt loads of lube between your thighs until it seeps between your legs, and sandwich his cock between your clenched thighs. He can then pump away as he would if he was inside you, and it's a similar sensation if you get your legs together tight enough. Have you ever been asked, "is it in yet?" That's how similar it feels.

This can be used for foreplay or again when you want to avoid full sex. (Be wary if this is the case though – it will get them going and you will have to work hard to make sure they don't try and sneak it in.)

For added tightness try crossing your legs at the bottom. You can alternate thigh sex with rubbing the tip of his penis against your bits.

You can also use armpits (I don't know how it came about but I experimented with this with my first long term boyfriend) and even bent knees… anywhere there's a join that bends, a cock can penetrate, so why not experiment? It should give you both a giggle.

TIP 81

The bum is another crevice for guys to explore. Get him to put loads of lubrication between your cheeks and masturbate between your bum cheeks. This is a good alternative to a 'tit wank'. It feels and looks very similar for a man. Careful he doesn't try and sneak it in your bum though – unless you want him to!

This was a request during my first unofficial 'escort job'. An unusual request, however I found it mildly arousing and unobtrusive. You can read more about this in my first book *The Girlfriend Experience.*

TIP 82

GETTING JUICY

Try tasting your juices: it can be a big turn on for your man to watch you seductively licking your juices from your fingers while looking at him in the eye. Alternate between doing this and displaying your bits to him for 'look but don't touch' teasing.

Try having one leg up with your foot down and tilting your pelvis forward to give him a better view. This will drive him wild and he'll be begging for you to move over his face for him to taste you himself. Lower yourself down on him and rub yourself over his face, and every now and then lift up, so he has to lift his head up to reach, then once again lower down.

N.B. Don't feel self conscious about how you taste – if he's down there, trust me you taste good! You can always put some lube down there if you feel you want to dilute your juices, however it's really not necessary as a healthy diet and no problems with your sexual health will ensure that you taste good.

ZINGY CITRUS MADEIRA CAKE

SAUCY FACT

Because of it's sweetness and naughtiness cake is a word sometimes used to describe female genitalia and sex.

Zingy Citrus Madeira Cake

TIP 83

Squelching: when you have a finger inside try putting only the tip in and flicking it out, or moving your finger from side to side keeping the hole visible so that your man can hear the sounds of your juices squelching inside you. Using lube when masturbating can give a similar squelching sound. This will really get him going.

TIP 84

Women – when you're wet, tell him how wet you are and/or, guide his hand down to feel your juices or slide up and down on one of his legs so that he can feel your wetness. Straddle him so that you are on his cock but he's not inside you, and slide your wet pussy along his shaft as it presses into his stomach.

If you get the angle right this can lead to a clitoral orgasm. After this he'll be begging for you to sit on his face – or let him inside you.

TIP 85

RUB IT IN

Give him a double-handed corkscrew. Sit between your man (facing him while he is lying down), and squirt a load of lube on his cock, or try this after he is wet from saliva after giving him oral sex. As long as he's wet, it'll work. Grab his cock like you would if you were going to climb a rope, with one hand on top of the other and both thumbs facing upwards. Then, wring his cock like you were wringing out a dishcloth, while at the same time moving your hands up and down as though you were giving him a standard hand job. This one will make you look like a pro! Try this whilst sitting between his legs facing him with your legs crossing over his. This works well if you add the suction hand job to the mix too.

Pate Sucree

PATE SUCREE

SWEET PASTRY

140g unsalted softened butter
90g caster sugar
1 large egg
270g plain flour

OPTIONAL SAUCY EXTRAS AND FACTS

Tarts are a great way to add in your fruit and chocolate aphrodisiacs. To make a chocolate pastry just add 30g of cocoa powder. Other aphrodisiac fruits include bananas, figs, pomegranate, pineapple, and even apples are now said to improve women's sex lives.

Either buy or make some crème patissière (the custard filling), spoon it into your case and decorate with the aphrodisiac fruit or fruits of your choice.

TIP 86

Women – use his cock to massage your clitoris. Make sure it's wet either from his or your saliva or lube, and masturbate with his cock. Use it as a finger and masturbate as you would if it were your finger. Circulate it and rub it up and down carefully avoiding penetration – until you're ready of course. It's a great way to have an orgasm and then easy enough for him to slip it in as you are coming.

TIP 87

MIX IT UP

Experiment with different sensations when you give oral sex. Have an ice-cold glass of water and a hot drink at the side of the bed. Don't use tea, coffee or alcohol because they dehydrate you and dry your mouth out. Instead, try herbal tea, hot water with some fresh mint leaves or even just hot water.

Take a few sips of the ice water or hold an ice cube in there for a few seconds, and then put your mouth round his manhood. After 30 seconds or so have a few sips of your hot drink and do the same. Alternate between the two. You can blindfold him so he doesn't know what's coming next.

BLACKCURRANT AND LIQUORICE SWISS ROLL

SAUCY FACTS

The smell of liquorice is said to stimulate male libido, whilst blackcurrants have some of the highest levels of zinc, which is essential for a healthy reproduction system.

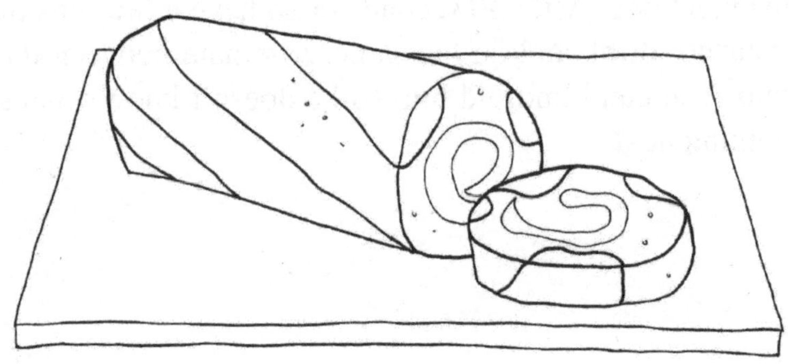

*Blackcurrent &
Liquorice Swiss Roll*

TIP 88

The balls shouldn't be neglected: as I've mentioned, they are extremely sensitive. Experiment with different sensations.

Some guys like nails lightly scratching. It's an area you need to be very careful with for obvious reasons which is probably why a lot of women avoid this area, but they do need attention. You can cup them, lick them, suck them, gently tug them and nuzzle them. It should be standard procedure to give them some attention if you are giving your man a hand job or blowjob. Enjoy the sensation of the soft skin.

TIP 89

It's worth working your pelvic floor muscles to keep them nice and tight *(not just for his benefit!)*. Simply clench and release your pelvic floor muscles (the ones that are all-important in Pilates) to enhance your own orgasm – and your lover's. You can do it at your office desk munching your lunch and no one will know.

Clenching the kegels will help women keep things nice and tight down there, which can enhance the feeling for both of you when you have sex. While he is inside of you, clench, so you are hugging his cock, the sensation will drive him wild!

Try tightening it as he thrusts in and loosening it as he comes out. As he is coming, clench as much as you can as it will intensify the feeling for him. If you want to know if you're doing it pop your finger in and feel. Men can tone their muscles too. Doing so can enhance their staying power and erectile strength.

TIP 90

DREAMY DELIGHTS

Fantasies: we all have them, and if you don't, you can have fun finding out what yours are!

For ideas try reading other people's fantasies (there is an abundance of erotic literature online now – try Cliterati.co.uk or Literotica.com). The ones that get you tingly down below are ones that you can use for yourself.

You don't even need to let him know, it could just all be going on in your head whilst you are having sex! The thing about fantasies is that they are just that. You can let your imagination run wild and he'll reap the rewards.

TIPSY TRIFLE

SAUCY FACTS

Alcohol will certainly relax you so a good measure in a trifle will help release inhibitions and stimulate libido. However drinking excessive alcohol will have the opposite effect and could make you anxious and/or unable to perform.

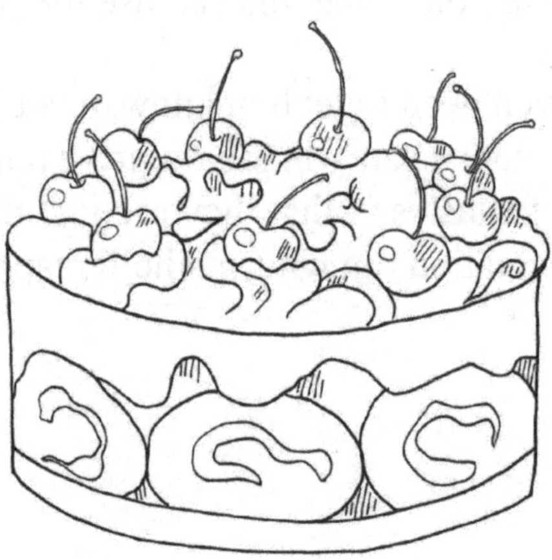

Tipsy Trifle

TIP 91

Just because you fantasise about something doesn't mean you want it to happen in real life (so dressing up in a school uniform doesn't mean he is interested in children.) Many guys are afraid to speak about their fantasies because of the reaction they think they will get from their partner. It's very important that if someone opens up to you about their fantasies, you don't make them feel embarrassed, perverted and/or weird, even if it sounds strange to you.

There are no boundaries with fantasy. The more open and comfortable your partner can be with you about sex and his desires, the less likely it will be that he will stray.

TIP 92

Find a way you can explore his fantasy and build elements into your sex life. Whatever happens though you must both be comfortable with the situation, and must never do anything that makes you feel uncomfortable, just to please your man. So boundaries and/or a safe word (a word you wouldn't usually use during sex that means 'stop' – as some people like to include mock-resistance in their fantasies) need to be discussed beforehand.

TIP 93

You can go the whole hog with fantasy and role-play; it doesn't just have to be an outfit in bed, you can get really creative.

One of my regular ex clients once printed out some photographs of an escort wearing a schoolgirl outfit and he superimposed other women in schoolgirl outfits behind, so it looked like I was being naughty in front of other pupils. He started the role-play at dinner where he produced the photographs, went into his role as head master and pulled out his improvised photos to ask, "what is the meaning of this?"– much to the embarrassment of the couple next to us. Once back in the room I had to perform various sex acts to avoid expulsion!

TIP 94

Innocent looking – dirty in bed. One way to catch him unawares is to dress innocently and then come out with something completely unexpected about what you'd like to do to him, or him to you sexually. This adds to the excitement of spontaneity.

TIP 95

Many men love a ditsy woman (even if it's just fantasy). It can be good for their ego, and make them feel manly and like an alpha male. You want him to feel this to get the best out of him as a lover.

This was mine and my first boyfriend's favourite thing to do…

For this role-play you plan to go to an out of town pub where no one knows you, and sit in the bar on your own. Get him to wait 5 minutes before going in. Sit on your own and he stays at the bar and you both pretend you don't know each other. You can start by basic flirting before he tentatively approaches and asks if he can join you. It's up to you where you go from there, but acting a bit ditsy makes the whole experience fun and not too serious. You can even adopt a silly girlie giggle.

The end to this is that he's pulled and you both go and have some mind-blowing sex, keeping in the role-play if you wish. If you're feeling bold you can find somewhere discreet outdoors. If you really embrace this role it can be so much fun!

TIP 96

You can also wear a wig to surprise your bloke. It's easier to pretend that you are someone else if you visually look different. So the more props the better. If you both dress up with hats, glasses and other props you can both really get involved, so get creative!

TIP 97

A FEAST FOR THE EYES

Watching women dance in a sensual way can be very erotic – and you don't need to be bisexual to appreciate the skill involved. Even if you look at it from a technical/acrobatic point of view, what they can do is incredible, and if you've ever tried pole-dancing you'll know it takes a lot of skill.

It's healthy to be able to appreciate women's beauty – and many men love it if you can appreciate attractive women too!

One thing you do need though is to be confident and secure in your relationship. This isn't a good idea for anyone who has jealousy or insecurity issues (but do read on because there is an alternative for you – Tip 100).

First, explain to your partner you're intrigued and suggest going to a lap-dancing club. There's no need to commit to having a dance. It's OK to go and watch to check you're comfortable in the environment.

Don't feel pressured by the girls to have a dance for either you or your man. Say it's your first time and you'd like to just watch for now.

If you don't take things any further, treat it as foreplay and go home and play with each other.

Tiered Macaroon & Sugar Dough Biscuit Centrepiece

TIERED MACAROON & SUGAR DOUGH BISCUIT CENTREPIECE

SAUCY FACTS

It has been reported that 93% of people across Great Britain eat a biscuit every day!

Whilst this particular recipe is somewhat extravagant, you might want to try making sugar dough biscuits on their own to dunk in your tea.

TIP 98

If you're comfortable to go to the next level, say you'd like a double dance, and you're going to pick the lady. Being assertive and taking the lead in this situation will be a big turn-on for your man if he likes the idea of you appreciating the ladies. The best thing about this is that you will find your man spends most of the time watching you watching the girl, than watching the girl himself!

It can be a turn-on for him knowing you are enjoying the dance. *NB – choose your lady carefully.* I recommend you ask the management who will perform best for women. Some ladies accept a couple's dance but they're not happy dancing for women, so give a poor show.

TIP 99

I've had some fun escort dates where we have gone to lap dancing clubs and I have had private dances before going back to the hotel to entertain my client.

To take things up another gear, say you'd like to be treated to a private dance out of view from your man, and watch and learn. His imagination will be running wild thinking about what you both might be getting up to! Call it market research.

These ladies know how to drive men wild, so don't hate them – respect and learn from them. If you're feeling bold, why not ask them for a few tips?

TIP 100

For those not comfortable with going to a club another option is to be the star of the show yourself. If it interests you, you can start pole-dancing lessons and learn how to do it. This will help you build your confidence, and you never know when, you are a whizz on the pole and can entertain your man (you can buy poles for your home) you might want to take him to a club another time.

TIP 101

Strip tease: as an alternative you can also get strip tease lessons or burlesque, both of which will work wonders for your confidence and help you ooze sexuality. There are also many clips on YouTube to give you tips and ideas.

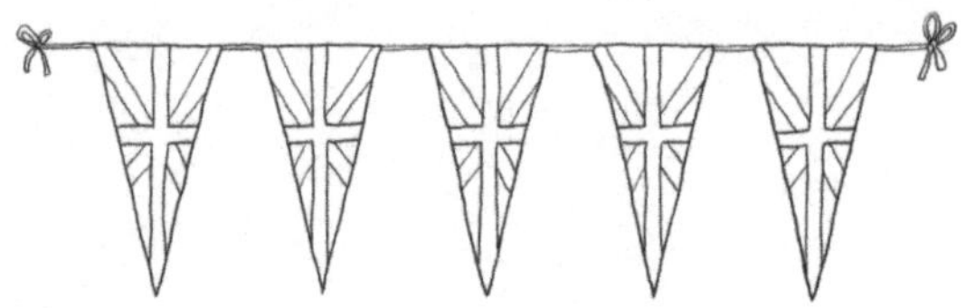

MIND YOUR MANNERS

While it's fun being rude, there are also certain matters of sexual etiquette that are all too common.

Don't worry – the Great British Sexpert is here to help you be polite while you play.

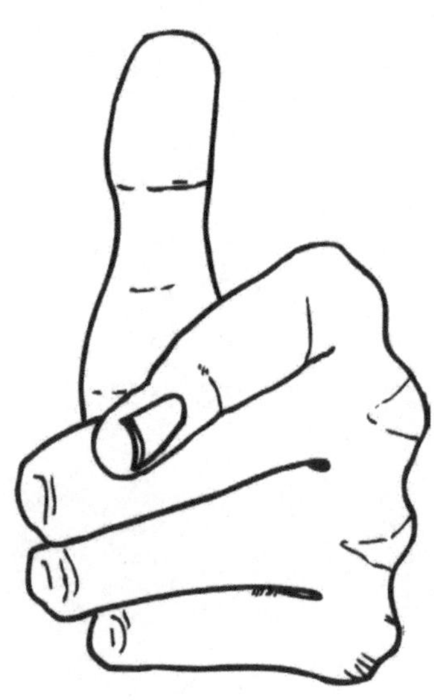

Queefing or Fanny farts: there are men that seem to think that fanny farts are like normal farts and that it's something we control; when it's actually men creating them by pumping women full of air. As long as we understand them we can learn how to avoid them.

They usually occur when someone takes their penis in and completely out of the vagina. It's almost like a bicycle pump. So be aware if someone is doing this, and try keep the penis tip fully inside, or just slow things down and test out if you can feel the air filling up.

Once the air is there it will come out during sex or after and make a loud fart-like sound. If you feel it's there you can excuse yourself to the loo, and take very small steps consciously trying to keep your legs close together so you don't make a sound. When you get in the bathroom cock one leg up on the toilet and put two fingers (middle and forefinger on the same hand) up inside you; once they are inside part the fingers to open the vaginal wall, and do your pelvic floors. You will be able to feel, but not hear the air expel. Then you can get back to business. If, like me, you're not embarrassed anymore then just deal with it there and then and have a giggle.

One of my most embarrassing moments ever was when I had just started having sex and didn't know they even existed. I was with an older guy and we were doing a 69, and it happened in his face!!

Real farts: so what do you do? You're in the middle of playtime and you have stomach cramps and you know that you need to fart. You might be in that comfortable relationship where it's not an issue and you can sneak one out and both have a giggle, or it might be that you are new in a relationship and don't want to be embarrassed by letting out any unsavoury sounds (and smells!).

There is only one way to discreetly release the discomfort and that is by pushing a tissue on your anus opening (whilst keeping your finger there), when you let the fart go. There is no sound because the tissue muffles it, and any smell is contained in the tissue. You may be able to discreetly do this under the cover when you're petting.

Sex during time of the month: yes it's messy but nothing that a few dark towels won't hide. Some men like to give oral sex during a woman's time of the month. Remember, using tampons he can comfortably and cleanly give you oral sex without any mess. Although some don't mind giving it without any sanitary protection; check first! Those in the sex trade use make-up sponges or natural sponge to stop the blood flow for sex during the time of the month; however, let me be clear that *this is **not** something I recommend and neither would doctors, as it's not hygienic and there is a strong chance it may get stuck and/or even lost and forgotten about which can lead to severe problems down below including a risk of infertility!*

Cock too big for you: it can be scary the moment you discover that your sexual partner has a large penis. Some women love them, but for many the reality is they are not very enjoyable, and can cause discomfort. It's imperative that you use lots of lubrication, for whatever you are doing, especially when it's going anywhere near your pussy. Don't be shy about using as much as you need. Lots of foreplay is needed so that you can feel relaxed.

Never endure any pain or discomfort during sex. Make sure that your partner is sensitive enough to take things at your pace. Try sticking to positions when you are in control of how far his penis enters you ie; on top. For oral sex, instead of trying to put all of his penis in your mouth try the techniques where you are concentrating on the penis tip, balls, suction, hand techniques and anal play. Also using his tip to masturbate your clitoris can be a way to work with a larger cock.

The pleasures of smaller penises: it is worth remembering that the average penis size is smaller than you actually think – 5.1 inches erect. Usually men with smaller penises are very good in bed or very willing to learn. They normally hone their oral sex techniques, whilst during penetrative sex they often reach areas that other penises can't. Close to the entrance of the vagina (internally) is a very sensitive area, and an area that gets bypassed most of the time when guys penetrate. With a smaller penis it can hit the spot every time. Remember, your G-spot is only a couple of inches up inside you. Use cock rings to maximise the size and make it look bigger. Oral sex can also look pretty impressive with a small penis as you can usually get all of it in your mouth. Men with smaller penises rely on technique, and can be more considerate lovers.

Circumcised: don't get freaked out when you see your first circumcised penis, it really is a beautiful thing.

Without the foreskin you don't do anything differently although for masturbating you might like to make it wet with saliva or lubrication to allow your hands to glide. All the penis pleasures I mention can all be done in the same way, except you're just not pulling any skin back. Some guys can be either more or less sensitive, so ask your partner or explore and find out.

Tight foreskin: if his foreskin is tight then don't try and pull it too far back as this will cause discomfort; if in doubt, let him show you how he likes to be masturbated. Some can pull the foreskin off the head of the penis and others can't. Generally if you treat it as circumcised without trying to pull the foreskin back this should keep things comfortable for him.

A curved penis: is extremely common, and shouldn't be treated any differently, you might be surprised at the areas it can reach that others can't! However if it's painful for him erect then he should see a doctor.

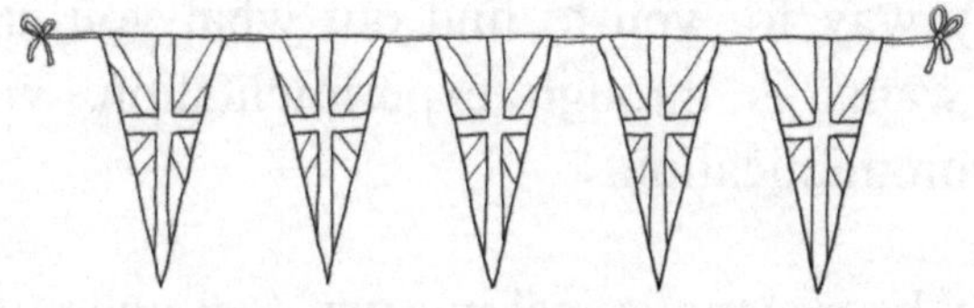

CONCLUSION

Satisfying sex is about finding someone who likes the same things as you on an intimate level. There is no such thing as the wrong way to perform an act of intimacy or sex providing there is mutual, adult consent.

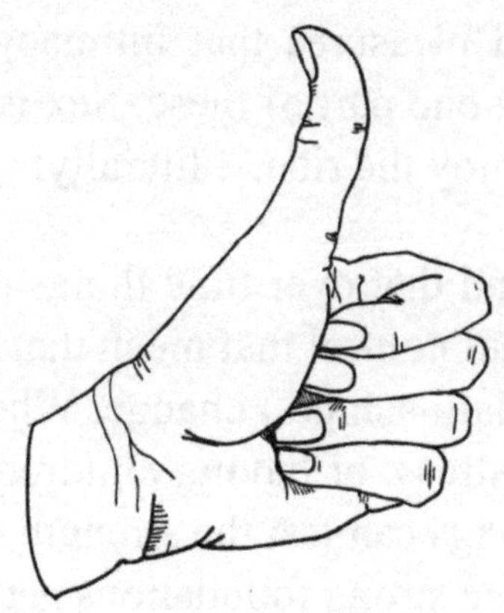

The only way for you to find out what you and your partner wants is through experimentation, via open honest communication.

If you feel someone is making you feel uncomfortable and/or embarrassed about sex when trying something new, or pressurising you to do something you don't want to do, or aren't ready for, then *they are not sexually and emotionally mature enough or sensitive enough to be a good lover for you.* Sex should make everyone involved feel good, even when things don't quite go as smoothly as you planned!

Try not to focus on having an orgasm, in fact my advice is to forget it, and just enjoy the moment, if and when 'it' happens it's a bonus. Some of my most memorable sexual experiences haven't ended in orgasm. Enjoy the sensations and pleasures that intimacy and sex offer; orgasm is only one part of these. Sex is a journey not a destination. Enjoy the ride... literally!

Do bear in mind that over time things can happen both in and out of our control that mean that the dynamics of your sexual relationship(s) change. Whether it's illness, bereavement, stress, or having children (to name but a few), many things can test the strength of a relationship and this is where strong foundations need to be in place, with communication, mutual respect, compromise care and understanding.

Healthy relationships are hard work and do take an investment of quality time to make them work and sustain long term happiness and fulfilment.

Time moves on, things change. Nothing ever stays the same. You can either choose to evolve, grow and adapt, embrace change and find a way to compromise so that on some level the relationship and intimacy works for all parties involved, or dig your heels in and be unhappy in your relationship (perhaps seeking pleasures elsewhere), or leave. I would strongly advise against using sex as a weapon in a relationship, because it's a slippery slope and usually ends up in infidelity and/or resentment.

Sex is about being in tune with your partner's physical and emotional needs. This is a two-way street. It is never one person's whole responsibility in a relationship to make sure the intimacy side of things stays intact. However, if each waits for the other, there's a risk that neither will start. With neither wanting to budge, the connection is lost, and sexual frustration may end up being expressed through arguing, aggression and frustration towards others, alcohol or other substance dependence, or infidelity – sometimes all of the above. When you choose to have sex it should be offered without resentment, expectation or any negative intention.

As a Sexpert, the biggest complaint I hear from men is lack of sex and boredom. This is not the fault of the partner but equally a breakdown of communication with neither getting their needs met. Interestingly my biggest complaint from women is that every touch has to lead to sex, so it's hardly surprising couples have problems in the bedroom!

I'm hoping this book has given you some ideas whether you're exploring sex for the first time, or wanting to try something new, or simply revisit some things that have been forgotten to reconnect with your partner.

Sex isn't something to be embarrassed or shy about, or even ashamed about. It's natural and can be a beautiful thing especially when there is a connection and meeting of the minds simultaneously. Sexual energy is the most powerful energy we have and we either use it or abuse it. You don't have to use it for sex, but if you don't, for it to be used in a positive way you need to consciously transmute (redirect) that energy. Some channel it into spirituality, some into their work/business, fitness, some into helping others. The suppression of it will lead to it being channelled in a negative way through frustration, anger, bitterness, resentment, and in some instances abuse of substances or other addictions.

By being willing to open up and explore your desires together, you can build intimacy and develop a closer connection. So get exploring: you never know what treats are there to enjoy until you try, and if you're ever in doubt...

KEEP CALM, CARRY ON AND HAVE A CUP OF TEA!

ABOUT THE AUTHOR

Rebecca Dakin is on a mission! As the Great British Sexpert she aims to help men and women from all walks of life embrace intimacy and rediscover pleasure in sex and relationships.

She went from convent schoolgirl to high class escort where she spent 10 years travelling the world and providing the ultimate 'Girlfriend Experience'. You can read more about her life in her first book *'The Girlfriend Experience'*.

As well as studying the seduction arts with Ross Jeffries and Neil Strauss, she is now a Master Practitioner in Neuro Linguistic Programming, a qualified practitioner of Hypnosis and Time Line Therapy.

Rebecca is a sought after expert in the media and has featured live on T.V's *Sky News* and their *Sunrise* morning programme. The pioneering new sex education series *Sex Pod* aired on *5Star* and featured her as one of the go-to experts answering questions from young people about sex and intimacy. She has also worked with Richard E Grant and has been invited as the Great British Sexpert to share her views with Rylan Clarke on *Big Brother's Bigger Bit on The Side*. Aside from her individual mentoring, she runs workshops and seminars to help men and women boost their body confidence and keep their love life on track!

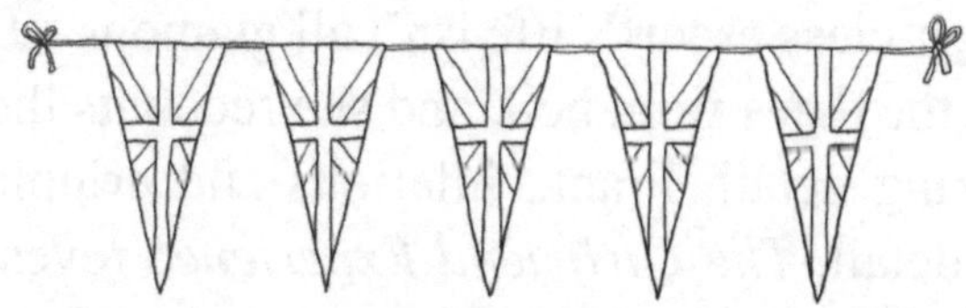

MORE FROM REBECCA DAKIN

THE GIRLFRIEND EXPERIENCE

My Sexploits as an Escort

What does it take to work as an escort? To offer strangers, companionship, affection and, most importantly, sex?

For almost ten years, Rebecca Dakin – known as Bea to her clients – provided what she called 'The Girlfriend Experience'. A date with blond, beautiful, passionate and outspoken Bea might involve romantic weekends spent at country houses, trips to Venice, Hong Kong and Dubai, five-star hotels, shared baths and candlelit dinners. Bea lived the high life, and gave her clients nights they would never forget.

But a high-class escort's life isn't all glamour – Bea also endured the dates from hell, and she recounts them here in shocking detail. Frank, hilarious and dripping with sensual detail, *The Girlfriend Experience* reveals what it's really like to work in this most misunderstood of professions.

"I recently worked with Rebecca on a series for BBC Worldwide and during that time I heard all about her fascinating life and book. I really enjoyed reading her book and admire her candour and honesty."

Richard E Grant
Actor, Director and Author

Available to download or as a paperback from Amazon or from www.thegreatbritishsexpert.co.uk

Turn over to read an extract...

CHAPTER FOUR – MY FIRST DATE

Even before I had my photos on the website I received a call for an overnight booking in Liverpool. Ade had contacted a guy who regularly saw the ladies on his site and had given me a glowing report, following which the guy insisted he saw me the very next day.

I broke the news to Mum and Dad that I was embarking on my first escort job and that it would be in Liverpool. They knew about the listings site, but obviously they didn't know that Ade had asked to sleep with me. To put their minds at rest, I truthfully told them that this particular client had seen loads of girls and was really nice, and that he'd booked us a table at a French restaurant. Neither of them tried to talk me out of it, they just accepted it – which is all they could have done, really. I think they were hoping I'd learn from my own mistakes, and maybe I wouldn't enjoy it and could then move on and get a proper job.

Mum agreed to give me a lift to the bus station, and I said I'd leave them full details of where I was going and who I would be visiting. They didn't ask me to do this, but I knew they would worry, so I decided I'd give them this information for every job I went on, for my own safety as well as for their peace of mind.

I called my friend Nat and gave her the exciting news. She wanted me to phone her as soon as I got back and give her all the juicy gossip!

So this was to be my first escort job. I was thrilled and excited, not nervous at all. I think this was mainly due to the fact that I'd had lots of reassurance from Ade about the guy – he'd seen so many girls and obviously Ade had had positive feedback. He was the perfect candidate to break me into my chosen profession. Had the booking come in from someone Ade didn't know, I think I would have been terrified.

It took me about two hours to prepare for the job. I think I was also subconsciously readying myself mentally; I wanted to look preened to perfection for him so I spent a long time bathing, shaving, moisturising and doing my nails. I picked out black, sheer lingerie with delicate pink bows. For a long time, I deliberated about what to wear, going through the garments on my rail, all of which were clubbing clothes. I wasn't about to wear my hot pants or rubber dress, and I didn't have any skirts or dresses that were on the knee or below, which left trousers as my only option. Most of mine were funky, tight, boot-cut flares. I had a leather-look pair and a snake-print PVC pair that I wore all the time. In the end, I decided on the leather-look, which I wore with some black platform boots, a tight black top and a dark denim jacket. I just didn't have any ladylike clothes – I didn't do ladylike. I did funky club wear.

Before arriving for the job, I decided I wasn't going to worry about it. I was surprisingly confident. As someone who genuinely enjoys meeting all sorts of people, this was the part I was looking forward to. I knew I was being paid for my time and that most of that time would be spent socialising, something that came naturally to me, so I wasn't nervous about my date. And I wasn't worried about the sexual side of things.

One thing I couldn't help but think about was how to make the move to the bedroom after our meal. I still wasn't sure, but decided to go with the flow. Being the chatty, open person I am, the conversational side of things didn't bother me at all. I knew I would be OK.

I had a forty-minute bus journey and then caught the train to Liverpool. The journey took about four hours. When I arrived at his house, I took a deep breath, put on a big smile and rang the doorbell. He invited me in – he was an accountant, average looking and in his forties, with glasses, dark hair and a medium, trim build. I remember thinking, 'If they all look like this and they're all as easy-going as this, the job will be easy!'

We went straight out to a nearby French restaurant. The meal was very tasty and the wine flowed. I couldn't believe I was being paid to have dinner with someone at a posh restaurant! I was totally overwhelmed by the whole experience. It was so exciting, I loved it! Thankfully, he didn't seem to mind my clumsy choice of attire.

Back at his house, we had a further drink and I suggested a game of strip spin the bottle, which made for a smooth transition to the bedroom.

I actually found it a quite a buzz that this guy was so in awe of me and willing to pay so much money just to be with me. We spent about an hour or so undressing and caressing, and giving each other oral sex. I was a bit of a show-off. The more he looked at me appreciatively, the more it made me want to perform. I wanted to be his ultimate fantasy. So, I writhed on the bed and teased him, looking up at him in a coy but suggestive way. I then straddled him and let his hands wander over my body. I used the tip of his penis to rub my clitoris, while I squeezed my boobs together to maximise my cleavage. I've always understood that men love visuals and women who are confident with their bodies.

I wasn't sure how long we should indulge in foreplay and I didn't know how long this guy was going to take to come when we had sex, or whether I should offer the condom or wait for him to ask. Eventually he asked me for one. My bag was in the other room! There's a learning curve, I noted to myself. So, I had to pause our playtime while I jumped off the bed, rushed out of the room to find my bag and fished about for a condom… all the while praying he'd still keep his erection! Once I had found one, I went back to the bed and sucked him again to get him back to his full erection before slipping on a condom, and getting on top of him. By this point he was so excited that he didn't last very long at all.

About 1 a.m., we went to sleep and in the morning we had a bit more sex, this time with less foreplay, before having breakfast. He said he really liked me and that he would want to see me again, and then he paid me cash in twenties: £700. I couldn't believe it! I had never held so much money in my hand before and I couldn't stop grinning. I was beginning to feel as though this job was my ticket to getting rich and living the lifestyle I had dreamed about.

A couple of months later he helped me to sort out my mortgage by confirming that I would have no problem making the payments, and we estimated how much money I would make for the year.

On the train home, I sat with a huge grin on my face, discreetly clutching the envelope in my bag and staring out the window, thinking, 'This is it – I'm finally on my way up!' I daydreamed about what my life would be like: I'd be one of those glamorous women in designer clothes, with perfect nails and hair, designer handbags and shoes, breezing in and out of posh hotels and restaurants, with slick businessmen taking me all over the world… First-class travel… Paris…

I rang Nat and left her a long, rambling voicemail about how I had found it so easy, and that I was buzzing and had £700 in my bag!

The first thing I did when I got home was to count the money, and put all the Queen's heads the same way, so they were neat. Then I counted it again… and again, before tucking it away back in its envelope. When Nat eventually called after she'd finished her boring nine to five job, the questions rolled in:

'You got how much?'
'What did he look like?'

'How old was he?'
'Were you nervous?'
'Where did you go to eat?'
'What was the sex like?'
'Was it difficult?'
'Did you fancy him?'
'Are you going to see him again?'

She was proud of me and said she could never do escorting. I remember thinking, it's no big deal, really… but I guess to most people it is.

Date: 18/19 November
Day of the Week: Sunday/Monday
Time of Day: 8p.m.
Time Spent: 2 overnight stays
Price: £1,400
Place: My hotel
Recommended: Yes
Would You Return: Yes

Description: The photos on Barbie's page are excellent, but don't do this beauty justice. She's around 5'8" with heels, and platinum blonde hair. Her figure is fabulous... she's a real STUNNER!!!!

Comments: I contacted Barbie easily by phone, and had a couple of phone conversations. She likes to weed out timewasters and after a couple of calls, a date was arranged. When Barbie turned up at my hotel (bang on time) I couldn't believe my eyes. What a babe, she is absolutely gorgeous!

Barbie confided in me that she was training to be a masseuse, and I was invited to her college as part of our date as she needed a volunteer to practice on. A relaxing massage was the perfect start to our overnight date! I was after the famous GFE, 'Girlfriend Experience', and Barbie offers this to perfection: lots of attention, lots and lots of love and tenderness, and forever asking if I was OK. Yes! What hot-blooded male wouldn't be?

Barbie has it all: the personality, looks, brains and sense of humour. She is an absolute joy to be with!

Guys, I am not going to go into the sexual side of things – all I will say is that I went home a very satisfied, content and happy man, the pinnacle of our time being bringing her to an orgasm on our second evening. There was no fake moaning and groaning here, this was for real!

You have to be prepared for people staring at you as a couple because of her drop-dead gorgeous looks. I enjoyed this immensely!

Barbie prefers the longer dates, rather than the two-hour 'wham, bam, thank you, Ma'am' because she likes to get to know people. This isn't her being greedy – she is just a very special lady who is very good at her job.

I can only say I wouldn't spend £1,400 on just anybody! I will be seeing Barbie again in January, and this will be my one and only review, gentlemen, as I can assure you, if you meet her you won't want to see anyone else either! Thanks, Barbie! Roll on the New Year!

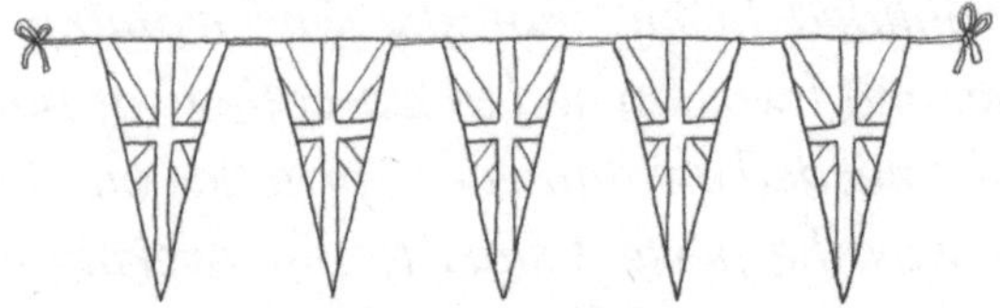

CONTACT REBECCA

www.thegreatbritishsexpert.co.uk

www.facebook.com/GBSexpert

www.twitter.com/GBSexpert

www.instagram.com/gbsexpert

www.youtube.com/user/RebeccaGFE

https:// uk.pinterest.com/rebeccamdakin